CW00545128

digital places

BUILDING OUR CITY OF BITS

Thomas A. Horan

FOREWORD BY WILLIAM J. MITCHELL

**Dedicated to the lives and memories of
Thomas B. and Patricia K. Horan**

Recommended bibliographic listing:
Horan, Thomas A. *Digital Places: Building Our City of Bits.*
Washington, D.C.: ULI–the Urban Land Institute, 2000.
ULI Catalog Number: D101
International Standard Book Number: 0-87420-845-9

Copyright © 2000 by ULI–the Urban Land Institute
1025 Thomas Jefferson Street, N.W.
Suite 500 West
Washington, D.C. 20007-5201

Printed in the United States of America. All rights reserved. No part of this book may
be reproduced in any form or by any means, electronic or mechanical, including pho-
tocopying and recording, or by any information storage and retrieval system, without written permission of the publisher.

CONTENTS

ACKNOWLEDGMENTS

THE WRITING OF *Digital Places* has been as much an ongoing and cherished engagement with colleagues as it has been a solitary writing experience. As denoted by the book's subtitle, the initial idea for *Digital Places* can best be traced to *City of Bits* by Bill Mitchell. I am grateful to Bill for the countless hours he spent with me during the summers of 1996 and 1997, when I used my sojourns to MIT to craft the initial concepts and themes for the book. As is apparent from his work (including the foreword for this book), Bill not only is a first-class thinker but also he is a master of the written medium. I am very grateful for his generous discussion both of the impacts technology is having on places and of the best approach to use in communicating this complex phenomenon.

My second intellectual debt is to Wendy Kohn, who came on board just when the manuscript was taking shape, or, to be more precise, when it needed to be editorially whipped into shape! Wendy came well equipped for a serious editing task—her formal training in architecture is second to none, and her written work with Moshe Safdie and others imaginatively captures the possibilities of design-inspired change. Where *Digital Places* rises to catch the nuance of physical design, where the writing perhaps hits its most sensate note, I have Wendy Kohn to thank.

Several talented researchers aided me in conducting numerous rounds of research and refinement of the manuscript. Early background papers and research were provided by Darrene Hackler and Kara Serrano, as well as by students in my various classes and colleagues at Claremont Graduate University (CGU) and elsewhere. This research stage of the book benefited from two roundtables on the subject, one hosted by the Lincoln Land Institute (with Ben Chinitz) and another hosted by Claremont.

Bob Dunphy played a critical role in bringing the project to the Urban Land Institute and facilitating a rapid review process, and the manuscript benefited greatly from the comments and insights of the ULI peer reviewers. Gayle Berens did a masterful job at engaging the considerable production talents at ULI to keep the publication on track. I particularly appreciate ULI's engagement of EngineBooks to copyedit the book. Abby Brussel picked up where Wendy Kohn left off and executed a skillful editing job that made the book better and left the author unscathed! Once the final inspection was made by her colleague Micaela Porta, the text was ready to go. Betsy VanBuskirk is to be thanked for the design and layout of the book, Steve Ducham and David Takasuye for gathering the photos, credits, and permissions, and Nancy Stewart for editing support during the later stages of the process.

Throughout the research and production of *Digital Places,* there have been various forms of financial support that deserve acknowledgment. An important source of support was CGU's Digital Communities project. I am grateful to Dan Mazmanian for his recommendation that I lead this effort, and to Esther Wiley from the School of Politics and Economics for her development work in obtaining grant support for this initiative from the North Star Foundation and elsewhere. Related research grant support recently came by way of my colleagues at the University of Minnesota, and I want to acknowledge both the direct and indirect support of Lee Munnich's State and Local Policy Program and Tom Fisher's Design Initiative. At Claremont, my new home in the recently established School of Information Science provided me with a fresh intellectual, physical, and, yes, digital setting to complete the work.

Finally, I must note that this four-year engagement with the ideas and people associated with *Digital Places* invariably took time away from my two wonderful children and my loving and devoted wife. One of the main themes of the book is recognizing what digital technology can and cannot provide. One of the things it cannot provide is the deep love of a caring family. My parents, to whom this book is dedicated, showed me that, and like all over-worked professionals I need to enact this value against the swells of work and opportunity. Enjoy the book—I'm off to play with my kids.

Thomas A. Horan

The Open Hand monument in Chandigarh's plaza.

FOREWORD

THE ELECTRONIC AGORA

William J. Mitchell

AT THE NORTHERN end of Chandigarh—Le Corbusier's famous monument of midcentury Modernist urban design—is a vast plaza with a gigantic open hand at its heart. It expresses a very beautiful idea, and it looks great in the drawings, but it just doesn't work. It's too big, too hot, and too far removed from the city's residential and commercial areas. Most important, it's too late; India's political discourse no longer takes the forms (if it ever did) of the agora-centered, face-to-face public debate that the scheme implies. In fact, political violence in public places has become such a concern that the plaza is largely ringed with barbed wire and under close military surveillance.

Symmetrically at the southern end of Chandigarh—in a messy industrial area that shows little evidence of planning—is another open hand grasping at the sky. This one is the dish of a satellite earth station, and it actually catches something—a stream of bits. Beside it, in an unimposing metal shed, reside racks of digital switching equipment. And behind the shed is a microwave tower that can beam data to any locations within line of sight, and

WILLIAM J. MITCHELL

A satellite earth station in Chandigarh's industrial zone.

receive incoming bits from those locations. This creates an invisible, imma-
terial, but very real *electronic agora*—a place within which digital information
can flow rapidly and freely, and can instantly be connected to the system of
global digital information flows. Within the electronic agora there are new
economic opportunities, new possibilities for the delivery of services, and new
potentials for social and cultural life.

Now consider California's El Camino Real—one of the oldest pieces of
urban infrastructure in North America. Its changing uses over the centuries
have reflected fundamental transformations in the ways that communities are
organized and interconnected. It began as a track connecting a chain of mis-
sions and carrying pedestrian and animal-powered traffic among them. In the
automobile era it developed, along much of its length, into a commercial strip;
the few remnants of the mission era were lost amidst the characteristic strip
building types—the gas stations, fast food outlets, drive-ins, and motels. Today, concealed beneath its surface, there is a fiber-optic backbone linking the
dot-coms, the new economic powerhouses of what has become Silicon Valley.
It is the same line on the map, but it now means something very different.

In 1994, at the very dawn of the dot-com era, I published a book entitled *City of Bits.*[1] In it, I began to ask what the digital revolution, as symptomized by these scenes, might mean for cities. I suggested that digital telecommunications networks would transform urban form and function as radically as piped water supply and sewer networks, mechanized transportation networks, telegraph and telephone networks, and electrical grids had done in the past. By supporting remote and asynchronous interaction, these networks would loosen many of the spatial and temporal linkages that have traditionally bound human activities together in dense clusters, and they would allow new patterns to emerge. We would see the fragmentation and recombination of familiar building types and urban patterns. And we would need to extend our conceptions of urban design to encompass virtual places as well as physical ones, interconnected by telecommunication links as well as pedestrian circulation and mechanized transportation.

Much of this was necessarily speculative, since only the beginnings of the new networks had actually been constructed; few people had much direct experience with them, and there had been little time for them to produce

A concrete scar reveals the presence of a fiber-optic backbone beneath El Camino Real in Palo Alto, California.

many real, measurable effects. (It was like writing about the effects of railways before the tracks had been laid.) But before long, we could observe complex processes of fragmentation and recombination in action.[2] Amazon.com quickly created a bold new spatial pattern of retail activity, for example. By shifting browsing and purchasing functions from bricks-and-mortar bookstores to cyberspace, Amazon radically *decentralized* customer-related activities, recombined them with homes and offices (wherever there was a computer and an Internet connection), and achieved worldwide, 24/7 coverage. Simultaneously, it *centralized* storage and distribution functions—thus achieving economies of scale—by creating huge distribution centers at airline hubs. And it *mobilized* back-office work—allowing it to take place wherever labor markets were attractive—by making extensive use of business-to-business electronic commerce technology. The resulting system of servers, networked personal computers, software, automated warehouses, and package-delivery vans bears little resemblance to the familiar Main Street storefront bookshop.

In *Digital Places: Building Our City of Bits,* Thomas Horan picks up the story at the dawn of a new century. He can look back on a tumultuous half-decade of digital infrastructure development (not so long, it might seem, but it's half a lifetime in Internet years), and a dot-com bubble of truly giga scale. He has telling examples to show, and a growing body of empirical data to rely upon. Most important, he has practical suggestions—grounded in experiences of success and failure—for designers and planners who seek to engage the problems and pursue the potentials of the digital electronic era.

Read it and learn, but don't imagine that the story of the "city of bits" is over yet. The differences between today and a decade hence will be as great as those between Sleepy Hollow and Silicon Valley.

NOTES

1   William J. Mitchell, *City of Bits: Space, Place, and the Infobahn* (Cambridge: MIT Press, 1994).

2   William J. Mitchell, *E-Topia: "Urban Life, Jim—But Not As We Know It"* (Cambridge: MIT Press, 1999).

digital places

BUILDING OUR CITY OF BITS

Where Have All the Drive-Ins Gone?

CHAPTER 1

THE RECOMBINANT LANDSCAPE

FOR SEVERAL DECADES, drive-in theaters embodied the widespread enjoyment of two technology-driven products—cars and movies—in a communal fashion we often lament as missing in today's public realm. Now, abandoned drive-ins litter the landscape, often creating desolate places of concrete, metal, and broken glass.[1] In many cases, theaters have been demolished, given way to new uses of precious land.

As captured in Jeff Brouws's stark photograph of Liberty, Nebraska, at left, the demise of the drive-in theater provides a metaphor for the fact that, at any given point, our social and physical landscape embodies but a moment in ever-changing technological circumstances: a technology comes into being, enables a set of economic and social activities, and then gives way to a new technological platform with its own set of behaviors and consequences. Drive-ins give way to home theater systems, banks give way to automated teller machines, and local factories give way to worldwide supply chains. In fact, a constant stream of technological advances has profoundly affected the urban landscape, including breakthroughs such as the railroad and car, high-

SWITCHES VERSUS PEOPLE IN LOS ANGELES

The emergence of telecommunications "hotels" in downtown Los Angeles is but one example of the many urban design challenges inherent in technology-driven change. Through much of the late 1980s and early 1990s, downtown Los Angeles witnessed an exodus of commercial office tenants from the core central business district. The exodus was due to a fundamental economic restructuring that occurred in the region (e.g., industry diversification, commercial office suburbanization) as well as a prolonged recession.[1] Parallel to this exodus, telecommunications firms began to quietly establish a "co-location" presence near the downtown telephone switching station. This presence mushroomed in the late 1990s because of the explosion in telecommunications demand coupled with the deregulation of the industry in 1996.

By 1999, there were approximately 150 telecommunications and Internet-related "switching" operations in the downtown core, many of which were occupying key commercial (and several historic) buildings.[2] One building, Wilshire One, has become emblematic of this urban trend toward "telco hotels" (see Figure 4.6), housing telecommunications equipment for some 100 firms. The equipment is connected through a sophisticated "meet-me" interchange room that uses a high-bandwidth connection to link with the local telephone switching station. While Wilshire One and similar enterprises have helped absorb once-vacant office space, they have also given rise to concerns about the vitality and diversity of city life as demands for telecommunication equipment compete with other people-based uses for downtown buildings.

Local broker Harold Sadowsky echoed the sentiment of many when he told the *Los Angeles Times,* "I have a great concern that this will become a downtown filled with a series of these factories. It's gone too far."[3] Shoemaker Chris Safarian expressed a similar concern when he told another reporter that the out-migration of people-based businesses could be felt on a day-to-day basis. "When these companies move out, there is a vacuum . . . I can feel the slowdown in activity."[4] And, in fact, the city has taken several steps to ensure a better balance of activities, from encouraging several educational establishments to occupy downtown space originally targeted for telecommunications tenants to fostering the development of several major "wired" live-work developments and other cultural amenities (including a $200 million Frank Gehry-designed Disney Concert Hall). ◄◄

1 See Edward Soja, "Los Angeles 1965-1992: From Crises Generated Restructuring to Restructuring-Generated Crises," in *The City: Los Angeles and Urban Theory at the End of Twentieth Century,* Alan Scott and Edward Soja, eds. (Berkeley: University of California Press, 1996). Also, Joel Kotkin, *Business Leadership in the New Economy: Southern California at a Crossroads* (Claremont, CA: La Jolla Institute, July 1998).
2 "Making Old Buildings New Again," *Real Estate Southern California,* November/December 1999, 33.
3 Jesus Sanchez, "Telecom Invasion Rattles Downtown L.A. Boosters," *Los Angeles Times,* 2 November 1999, A-1.
4 Daniel Wood, "Now There's Even Less 'There There,'" *Christian Science Monitor,* 20 April 2000, 2-3.

way and skyscraper.[2] These technologies have stretched the boundaries of cities both vertically and horizontally, from residential space sprawling across the landscape to office space pushing into the sky.

While technological development is, in part, undertaken for societal advancement, there is often a cost for such progress. Indeed, concern over technology's potential to overtake human desire has been a constant theme in American culture since the early days of the republic. Henry David Thoreau, Herman Melville, Thomas Jefferson, and others grappled with the impact of industrial-era technology on the pastoral culture of the country.[3] Today, postindustrial lament finds its place in the broken, dystopian visions of an entire school of work that includes writer William Gibson's *Neuromancer* and filmmaker Alex Proyas's *Dark City*.[4] Yale philosopher Karsten Harries captures a widespread sentiment when he observes: "Today our attitude to technology cannot but be ambivalent. On the one hand we know perfectly well that in countless ways technology has improved the quality of human life. . . . And yet, on the other hand there is the dread we feel at landscape being transformed into technoscape [and] at houses being converted into machines for living."[5]

And now, into our already technology-infused cityscape comes the digital revolution. Seemingly unconstrained by temporal or spatial limits, the rapid and continuing emergence of Internet-based technologies, networks, and services brings with it entirely new dimensions of electronically mediated experience and communication.[6] Will this virtual landscape make our cluttered public realm obsolete, so that we will no longer need to venture outdoors, content instead to surf the ubiquitous World Wide Web for all forms of work and pleasure? Will traditional cities meet the same fate as drive-in theaters? Will they be taken over by switches and telecommunications equipment "hotels" (see "Switches Versus People in Los Angeles," page 4)?[7]

DIGITAL PLACES: THE DANCE BETWEEN THE ELECTRONIC AND THE PHYSICAL

For enthusiasts of the virtual world there is little cause for alarm. Their vision is one of self-sufficient virtual cities that are far removed from the clutter and dirt of the physical world. As self-organizing collections of electronic communities and their cybercitizens, these nascent discussion lists, chat rooms, and virtual entertainment zones are developing their own aesthetic, their own culture, and their own history.[8]

While the virtual world of websites and chat rooms provides an intoxicating array of new experiences, it is not realistic to think that we can disassociate ourselves from our physical environment. Rather, the rise of cyberspace begs an examination of its connection to the physical world, the world of bricks and mortar. How and where do cyberspace and physical space intersect?

This book is about that intersection. It builds on several recent works that explore the impact of digital technology, such as the exhaustive three-volume *The Information Age: Economy, Society and Culture* by Manuel Castells; the Europe-oriented *Telecommunications and the City* by Stephen Graham and Simon Marvin; and, most relevant to the subject of digital places, the *City of Bits: Space, Place, and the Infobahn* and *E-Topia,* both by William J. Mitchell.[9] Each of these treatments integrates a range of perspectives, with the net result being a comprehensive examination of the interaction of telecommunications and the city.

Rather than attempt to replicate the formidable conceptual advances of these works, the point of departure here is more targeted and inductive—that is, I focus on "placemaking" activities and do so in a manner that focuses on unfolding events throughout North America.[10] My analysis does draw upon key insights made in these books—in particular, concepts such as MIT professor William Mitchell's "recombinant architecture"—to identify and capture salient elements of digital places, which vary in scale and character but share space in both the physical and electronic worlds.[11] Building on this notion of how technology facilitates the fragmentation and recombination of places, my aim is to analyze digital placemaking in homes, workplaces, libraries, schools, communities, and cities.

While my approach is inductive, it is not deterministic. I treat the emergence of digital places not as a phenomenon to be observed but as a development to be affected and improved by the application of appropriate design principles. I have assembled these principles under the rubric of "recombinant design" in order to present a set of guidelines that will help us interpret and, more important, plan for digital places.

Clues as to the nature of these design principles can quickly be spotted; they are revealed in our day-to-day activities and in the way these activities are arranged across physical and electronic space. For example, did you have more meetings or e-mail messages today at work? When was the last time you went inside a bank to get money? What would you want to change in your house or neighborhood if you had to work on a computer from home three days a week? Where would you live if your job allowed you to be anywhere so long as you had a high bandwidth connection? In the ensuing chapters, these and many other clues are followed to uncover evolving forms of digital places as they occur in the home, workplace, and community.

CONTINUUM OF DIGITAL PLACES

As just noted, the fundamental point of departure for this examination of the interweaving of virtual and physical place is the concept of digital places.[12] These are not stable end-states but dynamic settings that evolve over time. Given their evolutionary manner of development, digital places are emerging along a continuum of technological integration. At one end of the digital place continuum are "unplugged" designs that manifest little or no digital technology in their appearance and construction. Toward the middle of the continuum are various "adaptive" designs, representing modest attempts to visibly incorporate electronic features into physical spaces. Occupying the far end of the spectrum are "transformative" designs: rooms, buildings, or communities composed of truly interfaced physical and electronic spaces.

Despite what cyber enthusiasts may proclaim, unplugged places are still quite common and enjoyable, as digital technology has yet to significantly affect many settings. Many of our workplaces, schools, and public spaces were designed when "windows" were thought to be openings in a building for letting light or air through, rather than an operating system for opening the applications of a computer. For example, the bustling cafés that line the streets of Paris remind us of the enduring social and cultural value of such unplugged settings (see Figure 1.1).

USED WITH PERMISSION, NORMAN BARTH/LES PAGES DE PARIS (WWW.PARIS.ORG)

Figure 1.1. Unplugged design.

Moving across the continuum of digital places, we find many designs that have been modestly altered to incorporate some level of technology, but which retain their original organization and atmosphere. A common example of "adaptive" design would be a modest renovation of an office or classroom to accommodate personal computers. These designs often arrange the digital technologies in assembly-line formations, as in an elementary school classroom (see Figure 1.2). That most of the children in this photograph are peeking at their neighbors' screens demonstrates a significant point about this level of physical/electronic design: the design often does not attempt to integrate a full social and electronic program. In this case, using computers means that the entire class turns its back on the teacher. The introduction of digital technology into the physical environment often calls for a more fundamental rethinking of the activities to be conducted in the setting, and the best integration of technology to accomplish these objectives.

At the far end of the digital place spectrum are "transformative" designs, which are fundamentally organized around the demands of digital tech-

DIGITAL IMAGERY © 2000 PHOTODISC, INC.

Figure 1.2. Adaptive design.

nology systems. Still relatively scarce, and occasionally provocative, these are comprehensive designs that interweave electronic and physical components specifically in response to ongoing and emerging social interests and market demands for a more unified physical and electronic interface. As demonstrated in the Seattle-based Office of the Future project, innovative new arrangements between activity, technology, and design are possible. In this case, the office space entails innovative "commons" areas for informal collaboration, as well as flexible space for "heads down" work, all united by an integrated suite of wireline and wireless communications and computational and display technologies (see "Office of the Future," page 10).

These transformative designs are slowly emerging in a variety of settings, from innovative office plans to new forms of live-work environments and reinvented libraries and community centers. The central characteristic of these designs is their comprehensive integration of digital technology into the layout, program, and infrastructure of the place. Indeed, a central objective of this book is to outline directions and principles that can guide a more transformative approach to digital place design.

OFFICE OF THE FUTURE

Recognizing that seeing is believing, a consortium led by AT&T and Callison Architecture has sponsored a long-running Future@Work exhibit in 5,000 square feet of the Columbia Seafirst Center in Seattle.[1] According to Callison's Andrea Vanecko, "Future@Work provides real examples of new approaches to the workplace. The ability to experience the ideas first-hand—to touch, see, feel, and question the concepts—gives people a better understanding of what might or might not apply to their situation."[2] A central concept of the project is to expose clients to how space, technology, and people can be recombined to achieve innovative and productive new office arrangements. The exhibit does not advance a paperless, privacy-free office arrangement, but rather a thoughtful combination of public spaces, private alcoves, formal meeting areas, and informal hang-out spots. Paperless and freeform are passé, replaced by alcoves with storage for print material for concentration, meeting, relaxing, and (yes) sleeping.

Figure 1.3. Village Green space.

CALLISON ARCHITECTURE, INC.

As demonstrated by its Village Green space (see Figure 1.3), the AT&T/Callison design recognizes the value of informal meeting areas within the office setting. Similarly, the offices that lay beyond provide for more formal and concentrated work. In terms of technology, the exhibit features a wireless internal phone system that allows the phone to travel with the employee regardless of where he or she is located in the office. There is also a seamless network for connecting to simulated telework stations, as well as a variety of electronic presentation and interaction technologies located throughout the workspaces.[3]   ◀◀

1 The exhibit can be found online at: http://www.future-at-work.org.
2 Andrea Vanecko, "Office Design: You Don't Have to Know the Future to Get There," *The Seattle Daily Journal of Commerce* (13 November 1998). Available at http://www.djc.com/special/design98/10047033.html.
3 For a summary of the technology dimension of the Future@Work Exhibit, see William Karst and Douglas Johnson, "Technology, Design Will Make Office of Future Productive," *Puget Sound Business Journal*, 23 June 1997. Available at http://www.bizjournals.com/seattle/stories/1997/06/23/editorial3.html.

FROM SETTINGS TO CITIES

Digital places vary not only in terms of level of digital integration, but also in terms of the scale of integration. While the above vignettes of digital space design are at the scale of setting (e.g., café, classroom, workplace), digital places occur on multiple scales: homes and workplaces, communities, entire cities. And the scales interrelate: a digital setting can be part of a larger digital community located within a digital region.

The most intimate scale that concerns us, as in the case of the classroom, is known to ecological psychologists as a "behavioral setting." At the scale of the setting, a key design consideration is between people and their immediate built environment.[13] Alternative configurations can be devised to address the relationships of these spaces to the activities within them, the overlay of digital technology, and the social desires of the users of the space. A key objective is achieving, through function and aesthetics, a "sense of place," which psychologist Harold Proshansky defined as "a substructure of self-identity that defines an individual's personal identity in relation to the physical world through memories, ideas, feelings, attitudes, values, preferences, meanings, and conceptions about behavior relevant to the physical settings in his or her daily life."[14] In short, we have our favorite spots and they mean a great deal to us.

At the scale of a neighborhood or community, the design emphasis moves from fostering a sense of place to enhancing a sense of community. The critical role for digital technology at this level is to enhance the effectiveness of various community institutions (e.g., schools, libraries, community centers) as they seek to meet community needs and enhance the fabric of local interactions.[15] Electronic community networks can better link residents to these institutions and their services. More provocatively, these digital villages can provide new agoras for encouraging cultural, educational, and social interactions among community members. Early examples of electronic communities suggest that they can be deployed in a manner that stresses community-building. The Blacksburg Electronic Village provides but one well-documented example of how a local university (in this case, Virginia Polytechnic Institute) can foster a local network that connects schools, businesses, and residents and help to build a sense of community through its educational, social, and neighborhood-based content.[16]

Digital places at the regional scale are tremendously influenced by the overall character of the region's economic performance, digital infrastructure, amenities, and supporting public policies. Not every region has the same technical, financial, and educational infrastructure as Silicon Valley. Rather, high-technology development tends to identify the comparative "regional advantage" of an area, such as economic assets in banking (Charlotte), medical devices (Minneapolis), or new media (New York), and then forges public-private partnerships to enhance high-bandwidth infrastructures and supportive "soft" infrastructures (e.g., education).[17] Based on their analysis of several cities around the United States, Collaborative Economics, for example, has found that successful regions exploit not only their unique economic and technological assets, but also aggressively develop their business networks, their "regional culture," and the quality of the community in which the technological and economic development is to occur.[18]

In short, the digital technology revolution is creating new digital places at the setting, community, and regional levels. The challenge before us is to move from a passive observance of this phenomenon into a more active role in the design and development of digital places. The following principles of recombinant design are offered as a means to guide the development of these places.

PRINCIPLES OF RECOMBINANT DESIGN

Expanding upon William Mitchell's concept of "recombinant architecture," in which "telecommunication systems replace circulation systems, and the solvent of digital information decomposes traditional building types," the process of creating digital places can be thought of as "recombinant design."[19] Drawing an analogy between the recombinant DNA process and urban design, for example, recombinant urban design considers how digital technologies can be "spliced" into the recomposition of our homes, offices, communities, and cities to achieve optimal forms of space and place. That is, placemaking can be considered a deliberative and interactive process—settings, communities, and cities are constantly being reinvented based on a complex interweaving of economics, culture, technology, and circumstance (not to mention desire and resistance!). The concept of recombinant design focuses attention on how digital technology can be incorporated into this complicated yet important placemaking process.

Advances in the recombinant DNA process and genetic engineering (e.g., the human genome project) have also increased our need to link technological advances with ethical, social, and cultural issues.[20] Similarly, the task of integrating technology into our day-to-day places should not be left strictly in the hands of network designers, but rather necessitates the informed, active intervention of numerous parties including users, designers, and technologists. A firm understanding of the content, context, and values embedded in existing physical and social communities must guide each design decision.[21] As such, recombinant urban design must be considered an interdisciplinary process that crosses scientific, technological, architectural, political, and sociological boundaries to apply a broad range of perspectives to the development of digital places. In short, each of us should play some role in building our desired city of bits.[22]

At different scales of design, the impact of digital technology raises different sorts of issues; the design of a personal computer terminal presents a substantially different challenge from the design of a "wired" community. But like the DNA blueprint, there are distinct but elemental design principles at the core of recombinant design. How do, or would, these principles be applied at the local, community, and regional levels? Drawing upon a range of perspectives and disciplines, I have chosen four "strands" to focus this examination, as they appear integral to the process of recombining electronic and physical environments into satisfying digital places. These strands are: fluid locations, meaningful places, threshold connections, and democratic designs.

BRING E-SPACE TO PLACE: FLUID LOCATIONS

The first strand, *fluid locations,* refers to the need for place design to address the unprecedented spatial fluidity we now have to perform day-to-day activities anywhere and at anytime. As sociologist Manuel Castells has documented, the new electronic network has created a powerful "space of flows," the electronic movement of commerce and information that transcends individual physical places and provides an arena in which issues of power, conflict, and identity can thrive. These flows include, for example, the massive financial exchanges that sustain worldwide markets around the clock.[23] More recently, Castells observed that "the geography of the new history will not be made, after all, of the separation between places and flows, but of the interface between places and flows."[24] Like lightning touching down, these vast electronic networks ultimately connect somewhere in our day-to-day physical world. As related research by U.C. Berkeley's Matthew Zook has revealed (see Figure 1.4), these networks and related domain names (e.g., dot-com) are strongly associated with major economic hubs both in the United States and around the world.[25]

It is in this interface between electronic flows and physical places that digital places arise. From a design point of view, a key implication is the new communication and activity patterns that are unleashed by the space of flows.

Total Number of Domains

- 0 - 15,000
- 15,001 - 40,000
- 40,000 - 70,000
- 70,001 - 125,000
- 125,001 - 250,000
- > 250,000

©MATTHEW ZOOK

Figure 1.4. Global distribution of dot-com industries.

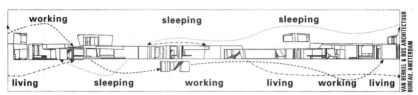

Figure 1.5. Residential activity flow.

Face-to-face communication remains an important part of our day-to-day activities but is increasingly supplemented by a host of new communication options. The widespread availability of Internet access has led to an explosion of computer-mediated communication, ranging from asynchronous, e-mail-style discussions to real-time chat and video-conferencing capabilities. The decreasing cost of telephony has further enabled our ability to work remotely.

How we distribute our activities along these new technology-enabled space and time dimensions will provide a subtle yet powerful guide for digital places. Where do we choose to go for face-to-face activities? How much of our jobs can be done through remote telephony or computer-mediated access and how does this affect the design of business, residential, and social places? The answers can affect the design of new houses (in terms of live-work spaces); workplaces (in terms of knowledge work and collaborative office design); and civic places (in terms of face-to-face and remote access activities).

The key to the fluid locations construct is to understand how digital places can be created to accommodate new communication and activity patterns. The design of digital places must not only accommodate these patterns but attend to other objectives of the built space, functional or symbolic. Figure 1.5 provides an example of this fine-tuned design; it is a flow diagram developed by Dutch architect Ben van Berkel to illustrate how he designed a house that integrates work, living, and social spaces for two professionals.

A NEW SENSE OF PLACE: MEANINGFUL PLACES

The notion of *meaningful places* embodies the need to design digital places in a manner that respects the functional and symbolic associations that places often contain.[26] From a community design perspective, we need to consider how increasing use of digital technologies affects our perception and use of the physical and social communities that surround us. An oft-cited criticism of cyberspace has to do with its possible adverse implications for our sense of place and community. For some, the ability to communicate with anyone from anywhere also means that we are nowhere—that is, dislocated agents not really connected to any person or place.[27]

Cognitive researchers agree that a sense of place is an anchoring feature of satisfying urban environments.[28] Anthropologist Ray Oldenburg, for example, argues the importance of what he calls "third places" that augment home and work: the coffee shops, community centers, and hangouts in cities and towns that serve as hubs for real-time personal exchange.[29] As the global village fast becomes reality for many of us, one of our greatest challenges will be to forge strong, parallel links with the enduring qualities of local, physical

Figure 1.6. Connecting meaningful space and place.

community. There is a need for digital places that will function like front stoops of the past but now will be built as a synergistic combination of physical place and cyberspace.

Early examples of such "virtual behavior settings" were the electronic chat groups—such as the Well—formed around topic areas.[30] Now, new electronic forums are possible that connect virtual environments with physical communities.[31] For example, several urban, suburban, and rural communities in North America have established electronic networks that serve to encourage (through bulletin boards, chat rooms, newsletters) face-to-face interactions among neighborhood residents.[32] In London, a preliminary trial by Microsoft found that such networks can increase informal social exchange by residents.[33] Moreover, these electronic forums can utilize traditional neighborhood landmarks, such as libraries and community centers, to ensure universal access by community members. In New York, the Settlements project combines virtual communities and historical "settlement houses"[34] (early neighborhood centers) to enhance a sense of place, history, and community in the city (see Figure 1.6).

TRANS-AESTHETICS: THRESHOLD CONNECTIONS

The design aesthetic of the digital era continues to evolve with each new website and feather-light laptop. The third strand of recombinant design, *threshold connections,* focuses on the need to design cognizant of the relationships between physical and virtual space. There are two dimensions to this strand: the reflection of the virtual aesthetic in the physical environment and what Stanford's Terry Winograd, a computer scientist, has referred to as the "interspace" between the physical and electronic environment.[35]

As to the reflection of the digital era on the physical environment, the emergence of a digital aesthetic comes at a time when there is no one reigning architectural style. Today, projects range stylistically from nostalgic vernacular to classicist postmodern, from cool modernist to brashly disordered deconstructivist.[36] The term "trans-architecture" has been advanced by architect and theorist Marcos Novak and others to suggest a design approach that transcends any given aesthetic orientation and freely incorporates any style or form deemed appropriate to the context and objectives of the design project.[37]

Threshold connections extend the idea of trans-architecture to consider the interface between physical and electronic design aesthetics. This new aesthetic refers to achieving a condition of translucency for the transitions between electronic and physical spaces. When we move from one realm into the other, our passage should be as seamless, easy, and clean as we can possibly make it. For instance, several new interactive science museums (e.g., the Exploratorium in San Francisco, the Computer Museum in Boston)[38] have created vibrant digital places where children learn about science through an interwoven electronic and physical experience.

The purpose of this strand is to encourage us to address the physical setting in which the electronically mediated activity is going to occur. This can be in the form of a setting that, for example, focuses attention on the electronic task by providing an unadorned background. Conversely, settings can evoke a provocative stylistic contrast, such as the New York Science, Industry, and Technology Library in Manhattan. "The contrast between the 1906 Renaissance Revival façade and the elegant modernist interior," explain the library's architects, Gwathmey Siegel & Associates, "reflects the balance between the library's nineteenth-century origins as the temple of wisdom and its twenty-first century role as an emporium of rapidly changing information."[39] Now that's contrast (see Figure 1.7).

The heart of the threshold connections issue is not the style of the room or screen design, however, but the relationship between constituent parts: where the user sits (e.g., solitary or group environment); what the user interacts with (text-based, two-dimensional, or three-dimensional virtual representation); and what combination of activities—real and digital—are made possible in the "interspace" between the physical and electronic. Different approaches are still emerging for this relationship, which has ranged from highly virtual environments that often ignored the physical environment to more integrated efforts to connect electronic space to physical places. For example, Yahoo's GeoCities used to be organized by "neighborhoods" (e.g., Bourbon Street), but recently abandoned the physical metaphor for more placeless clubs.[40]

Figure 1.7. New York Science, Industry, and Technology Library.

Community and culturally based electronic networks almost by their definition can be designed to display a stronger connection to physical community (albeit with simpler graphical and text-based formats).[41, 42] For example, a recent evaluation of a local online arts community found that participants felt the electronic community enhanced participation in local arts activities.[43] A successful example of this is Echo Salon in New York City, which provides a range of online discussion groups and happenings for its predominantly local participants.[44] While more exotic three-dimensional representations of physical places remain promising, they have yet to take off in mainstream online communities.

Figure 1.8. Echo Salon home page.

ACCESS TO BITS: DEMOCRATIC DESIGNS

The fourth construct, *democratic designs,* is about the process by which we design digital places. To create a sense of place and community, by definition, begs a process that involves those whose places and communities will be affected. "Transformative" urban design experiments and "revolutionary" technologies fail time and again specifically because the relevant parties were not engaged or consulted.[45] Nuclear power plants in the technology arena and Pruitt-Igoe housing in the urban development arena are but two high-profile examples of failures relating, in part, to technical/user mismatches.[46] In the workplace, the impact of advanced technologies on productivity has been found to vary dramatically depending on a variety of social, economic, and organizational factors.[47] A landmark National Science Foundation study found that user involvement in technology implementation was a critical factor in the success of these innovations.[48]

Political scientist Langdon Winner has been an eloquent champion of an open decisionmaking process for technology. "We should try," he writes, "to imagine and seek to build technical regimes compatible with freedom, social justice and other key political ends. . . . Faced with any proposal for a new technological system, citizens or their representatives would examine the social contract implied by building that system in a particular form. They would ask, How well does the proposed condition match our best sense of who we are and what we want this society to be? Who gains and who loses power in the proposed change?"[49]

Democratic design is an essential strand for truly integrating our physical and digital environment because it originates directly from the combination of the technical capabilities required by digital systems and the interests and concerns of those who will occupy this new realm, including users, residents, e-consumers, digital product manufacturers, voters, citizens, and policymakers. In some ways, this will be enacted by ensuring high bandwidth access to customers and residents. In other ways, this can be accomplished by tailoring digital places to certain niche needs, such as community networks for the elderly.

Because the private marketplace will rightfully exert a strong influence on the style and accessibility of digital places, there is a parallel public need to ensure that these places are available across all segments of society.[50] A recent report by the U.S. Department of Commerce highlights the importance of considering the plight of all groups in this debate.[51] As portrayed in Figure 1.9, computer use and access still remain mostly a predilection of the more well off, with continuing differences occurring among U.S. residents of different ethnic backgrounds. The recombinant design approach explicitly addresses the need to involve a wide range of stakeholders in the design of digital places—a necessary condition for ensuring access.

A GENTLE MANIFESTO FOR DIGITAL PLACES

The four strands of recombinant design constitute a "gentle manifesto" for considering how digital technologies can be used to improve the way we live in the places where we live.[52] Simply put, we need to create places that comprehensively integrate human and technological elements in a manner that both respects and stretches our traditional notions of place, in a way that links both electronic and physical networks, and through a process that engages a spectrum of participants.

The design of buildings and cities has always been affected by the relationship between people's desires and extant constraints. The recombinant landscape will be a collage of settings which, properly designed, will advance the symbiotic relations between people and technology. We must nurture digitally infused change in a manner that produces the most satisfying shapes, forms, and experiences we can invent. At the same time, we must be careful

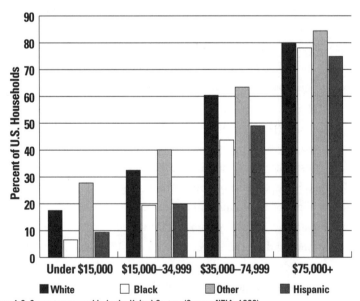

Figure 1.9. Computer ownership in the United States. (Source: NTIA, 1999)

to avoid making a technoscape of mediocrity that fails to facilitate communication or community.

To this end, the principles of recombinant design are offered as an analytical prism through which the impacts of digital technology on physical spaces can be brought into focus. In the terminology of systems design, these are high-level objectives or system requirements. The process aims to integrate the often disjointed activities of planners, architects, telecommunications providers, and public policymakers. The goals of recombinant design fit into a broader concept of design, a concept that engages a wide range of users and decisionmakers in designing and creating communities that meet their collective aspirations and expectations.[53]

As we explore provocative applications of these principles in the following chapters, the limitations of digital places must also be kept in mind. Digital places will never obviate the primacy of face-to-face interactions and experiences. There appears to be a natural law in operation: The need for human interaction is neither created nor destroyed, but merely and significantly altered by digital technologies. Rather, digital places are new leverage points for creating new experiences and relationships that will profoundly redefine our experience of physical space. As writer Edward Rothstein once observed, "Whether it is heading toward apocalypse or utopia, technology seems to have the power to move us, to create a sense of change. No other aspect of contemporary life has that character."[54] The following chapters examine this movement, with an eye to how it might be guided to create gratifying and enduring experiences and communities.

NOTES

1   See Maggie Valentine, *The Show Starts on the Sidewalk: An Architectural History of the Movie Theatre Starring S. Charles Lee* (New London, CT: Yale University Press, 1994).

2   Chronicled in Kenneth T. Jackson, *Crabgrass Frontier: The Suburbanization of the United States* (New York: Oxford University Press, 1985).

3   See Leo Marx, *The Machine in the Garden: Technology and the Pastoral Ideal in America* (Cambridge: MIT Press, 1967).

4   See Robert Warren et al., "The Future of the Future in Planning: Appropriating Cyberpunk Visions of the City," *Journal of Planning Education and Research* 18 (1998): 49-60.

5   Karsten Harries, *The Ethical Function of Architecture* (Cambridge: MIT Press, 1997).

6   See William J. Mitchell, *E-Topia* (Cambridge: MIT Press, 1999), ch. 1.

7   See Jesus Sanchez, "Telecom Invasion Rattles Downtown L.A. Boosters," *Los Angeles Times,* 2 November 1999, A-1.

8   See Sherry Turkle, *Life on the Screen: Identity in the Age of the Internet* (New York: Simon & Schuster, 1995) for a classic inquiry into the virtual life. A more recent collected edition on this theme is John Beckmann, ed., *The Virtual Dimension: Architecture, Representation, and Crash Culture* (New York: Princeton Architectural Press, 1998).

9   Manuel Castells, *The Information Age: Economy, Society and Culture,* vol. 1-3 (Oxford: Blackwell, 1996, 1997, 1998); Stephen Graham and Simon Marvin, *Telecommunications and the City. Electronic Spaces, Urban Places* (London: Routledge, 1996); William J. Mitchell, *City of Bits: Space, Place, and the Infobahn* (Cambridge: MIT Press, 1995); William J. Mitchell, *E-Topia* (Cambridge: MIT Press, 1999).

10 While the focus of this book is on North America, similar developments appear to be unfolding in Europe and Asia. Stephen Graham in *Telecommunications and the City* and elsewhere has written extensively on Europe. Asian developments have been covered by several authors, including Kenneth Corey and John Langdale.

11 First introduced in Thomas Horan, "Planning Digital Places: A New Approach to Community Telecommunications Planning and Deployment," in *Handbook of Public Information Systems,* G. David Garson, ed. (New York: Marcel Dekker, 2000).

12 The term "digital place" is also used in Michael Curry, *Digital Places: Living With Geographic Information Technologies* (London: Routledge, 1998), though the reference here is on the connection between geographical information systems and geography.

13 Amos Rapoport, *The Meaning of the Built Environment: A Nonverbal Communication Approach* (Tucson: University of Arizona Press, 1990).

14 Harold Proshansky, "The Pursuit of Understanding: An Intellectual History," in *Environment and Behavior Studies: Emergence of Intellectual Traditions,* Irwin Altman and Keith Christensen, eds. (New York: Plenum, 1990).

15 Kevin Lynch, *The Image of the City* (Cambridge: MIT Press, 1960).

16 Anita Blanchard and Thomas Horan, "Virtual Communities and Social Capital," in *Social Science Computer Review* 16 (1998): 293-307; Douglas Schuler, *New Community Networks: Wired for Change* (New York: ACM Press, 1996). See "Chapter 3: Recombinant Architecture," in William J. Mitchell, *City of Bits* (Cambridge: MIT Press, 1995).

17 See AnnaLee Saxenian, *Regional Advantage: Culture and Competition in Silicon Valley and Route 128* (Cambridge: Harvard University Press, 1996).

18 Collaborative Economics, *Innovative Regions: The Importance of Place and Networks in the Innovative Economy* (Palo Alto, CA: Heinz Endowment, October 1999).

19 See "Chapter 3: Recombinant Architecture," in William J. Mitchell, *City of Bits* (Cambridge: MIT Press, 1995).

20 For an engaging overview of the human genome project, see Matt Ridley, *Genome: The Autobiography of a Species in 23 Chapters* (New York: HarperCollins, 2000).

21 For an example of evolving building design and use over the last century, see Stewart Brand, *How Buildings Learn: What Happens After They're Built* (New York: Penguin Books, 1994).

22 For a stinging critique of non-democratic attempts at community change, see James C. Scott, *Seeing Like a State: How Certain Schemes to Improve the Human Condition Have Failed* (New Haven: Yale University Press, 1998).

23 Manuel Castells, *The Rise of the Network Society,* vol.1 of *The Information Age: Economy, Society and Culture* (Oxford: Blackwell, 1996).

24 Manuel Castells, "Grassrooting the Space of Flows," in *Cities in the Telecommunications Age: The Fracturing of Geographies,* James O. Wheeler, Yuko Aoyama, and Barney Warf, eds. (London: Routledge, 2000).

25 Matthew Zook, "Internet Cities of the United States and the World: Understanding New Geographies" (Paper delivered at the Cities in the Global Information Society Conference, Newcastle upon Tyne, UK, 22-24 November 1999).

26 Among the many treatments of this subject are classics such as Kevin Lynch, *The Image of the City* (Cambridge: MIT Press, 1960); Tony Hiss, *The Experience of Place* (New York: Knopf, 1990). More practice-oriented treatments include Stephen Carr, et al., *Public Space* (Cambridge: Cambridge University Press, 1992); and William Morrish and Catherine Brown, *Planning to Stay: Learning to See the Physical Features of Your Neighborhood* (Minneapolis: Milkweed Press, 1994).

27 See Joshua Meyrowitz, *No Sense of Place: The Impact of Electronic Media on Social Behavior* (New York: Oxford University Press, 1985); Neil Postman, *Technopoly: The Surrender of Culture to Technology* (New York: Vintage, 1992).

28 While a consensus exists about the value of "sense of place," the definition of what this means varies considerably. Bill Hubbard, *A Theory for Practice: Architecture in Three Discourses* (Cambridge: MIT Press, 1995) provides the most cogent definition.

29 Ray Oldenburg describes "third places" as those places that are between the intimacy of the family and the anonymity of the street; they create a sense of belonging and of being known. Ray Oldenburg, *The Great Good Place: Cafés, Coffee Shops, Community Centers, Beauty Parlors, General Stores, Bars, Hangouts and How They Get You Through the Day,* 2nd ed. (New York: Marlowe & Company, 1997).

30 Howard Rheingold, *The Virtual Community: Homesteading on the Electronic Frontier* (Reading, MA: Addison-Wesley, 1993).

31 Anita Blanchard and Thomas Horan, "Virtual Communities and Social Capital," in *Social Science Computer Review* 16 (1998): 293-307. Also, Stephen Graham, "Cyberspace and the City," *Town and Country Planning,* 64 (8), 198-201.

32 Douglas Schuler, *New Community Networks: Wired for Change* (New York: ACM Press, 1996).

33 Bruno Giussani, "A Year and a Half Later, a Wired Neighborhood Looks Back," *New York Times,* 13 October 1998. http://www.nytimes.com/library/tech/98/10/cyber/eurobytes/13euro.html.

34 Settlement houses were large tenements in New York that provided housing for immigrants in the early 1900s. For an online exhibition on the history of New York settlement houses, see http://gateways.unhny.org/unh_exhibit/.

35 Terry Winograd, "From Computing Machinery to Interaction Design," in *Beyond Calculation: The Next Fifty Years of Computing,* Peter Denning and Robert Metcalfe, eds. (New York: Springer-Verlag, 1997), 149-162.

36 Kenneth Frampton, ed., with Arthur Spector, *Technology, Place & Architecture: The Jerusalem Seminar in Architecture* (New York: Rizzoli, 1998).

37 Marcos Novak, "Trans-architecture Presentation" (Getty Museum Symposium on Trans-architecture: Visions of Digital Communities, Brentwood, California, 5 June 1998).

38 See *Journal of the American Society for Information Science, Special Issue: When Museum Informatics Meets the World Wide Web* 51, no. 1 (1999).

39 Otto Riewoldt, *Intelligent Spaces: Architecture for the Information Age* (London: Laurence King, 1997), 222.

40 Anita Blanchard, "Virtual Behavior Settings: An Application of Behavior Setting Theories to Virtual Communities" (Unpublished manuscript, Claremont Graduate University, 1997); and Daniel Stokols, "Human Development in the Age of the Internet," in *Assessment of the Environment Across the Lifespan,* S.L Friedman and T.D. Wachs, eds. (Washington, D.C.: American Psychological Association, 1999).

41 Steven Johnson, *Interface Culture: How New Technology Transforms the Way We Create and Communicate* (New York: HarperEdge, 1997).

42 Peter Anders, "Envisioning Cyberspace: The Design of Online Communities," in *The Virtual Dimension: Architecture, Representation, and Crash Culture,* John Beckmann, ed. (New York: Princeton Architectural Press, 1998); Craig Calhoun, "Community without Propinquity Revisited: Communications Technology and the Transformation of the Urban Public Sphere," *Sociological Inquiry* 68, no. 3 (August 1998): 373-397.

43 Anita Blanchard and Thomas Horan, *Evaluation of LA Culture Net* (Claremont, CA: Claremont Graduate University Research Institute, 1999).

44 See Stacy Horn, *Cyberville: Clicks, Culture, and the Creation of an Online Town* (New York: Warner Books, 1998). Echo website is http://www.echonyc.com.

45 See Russell Ellis and Dana Cuff, eds., *Architects' People* (New York: Oxford University Press, 1989).

46 See Peter Hall, *Great Planning Disasters* (London: Weidenfeld and Nicolson, 1980). Also James C. Scott, *Seeing Like a State: How Certain Schemes to Improve the Human Condition Have Failed* (New Haven: Yale University Press, 1998).

47 Erik Brynjolfsson and Shinkyu Yang, "Information Technology and Productivity: A Review of the Literature," *Advances in Computers,* Academic Press 43 (1996): 179-214.

48 Louis G. Tornatzky and Mitchell Fleischer, eds., *The Processes of Technological Innovation* (Lexington, MA: Lexington Books, 1990).

49 Langdon Winner, *The Whale and the Reactor: A Search for Limits in an Age of High Technology* (Chicago: University of Chicago Press, 1986), 55-56.

50 Richard Sclove, *Democracy and Technology* (New York: Guilford Press, 1995).

51 National Telecommunications and Information Administration, *Falling Through the Net: Defining the Digital Divide, A Report on the Telecommunications and Information Technology Gap in America* (Washington, D.C.: U.S. Department of Commerce, July 1999).

52 The phrase "gentle manifesto" is taken from Robert Venturi's opening to *Complexity and Contradiction in Architecture* (New York: Museum of Modern Art, 1966).

53 Donald A. Schon and Martin Rein, *Frame Reflection: Toward the Resolution of Intractable Policy Controversies* (New York: Basic Books, 1994).

54 Edward Rothstein, "Ideas and Trends: The Future Works, Sometimes," *New York Times,* 23 February 1997, sec. 4, 14.

The Enduring Value of Settings: "Main Street," Nortel Networks headquarters.

CHAPTER 2

EXPERIENCING DIGITAL SETTINGS

OUR IMMEDIATE SURROUNDINGS crucially affect the quality of our experiences: we seek a good table at the local restaurant; just the right ambience for important business meetings; the right layout, light, and view for a new house or apartment; the perfect spot for a romantic getaway. Our ability to move through space—both to experience settings in the moment and, later, to remember their shapes, sounds, smells, colors, and light in our mind's eye—helps to define our sense of place. Through digital technology, as philosopher Edward Casey remarks in his comprehensive treatment of place, *The Fate of Place,* this age-old experience is brought to the fore: "It is almost as if the ancient dialectic of space and place is being replayed within the domain of technology itself!" he writes. "When life becomes significantly accelerated, we find ourselves more, not less, appreciative of the places we are so rapidly passing through."[1]

As introduced in Chapter 1, the focus of recombinant urban design at the intimate level of the "setting" is the interaction between a person and the immediate built environment, and how this experience is mediated, altered, distorted, or enhanced by new digital technologies. Drawing upon the strands of recombinant design, the issues become: how do we design settings in light of the *fluidity* of our activities? Do traditional settings, such as home and office, still have *meaning* in this increasingly converged environment? What new electronic and physical *thresholds* are created between e-commerce and more traditional bricks-and-mortar establishments? Is there any reason to believe those informal public settings, or "third places," will be *valued* in the era of virtual living?

Chapter 2 explores these questions within the context of our day-to-day settings; our movements provide important clues about spaces that are becoming obsolete and those that are evolving into new and intriguing digital settings. As Peter Drucker observes, "In human affairs . . . it is pointless to predict the future, let alone attempt to look ahead 75 years. But it is possible—and fruitful—to identify major events that have already happened, irrevocably, and that will have predictable effects in the next decade or two. It is possible, in other words, to identify and prepare for the future that *has already happened.*"[2] While the gamut of daily activities is wide, the chapter focuses on three core areas—activities in the home, in the workplace, and in the consumer retail environment. Taken together, our changing habits in these areas are causing subtle but "irrevocable" recombinations of physical and electronic elements that lead to emerging digital place possibilities.

HARMONY AND COMPLEXITY IN THE SETTING

A key ingredient in the success of new setting designs is appreciating the concept of setting complementarily—that is, a complementary set of activities within a specific environment.[3] If you have witnessed the social awkwardness of several people talking simultaneously on cellular phones while seated around a conference or dinner table, you have probably experienced the conflict created by juxtaposing an intimate electronic activity against a communal physical setting. Likewise, if you have worked on a laptop in a quiet corner of a café, you know how well electronic activity and public space can complement one another. Traditional adherence to building typologies (a bank looks and feels one way; a home, another) differentiates settings spatially, functionally, and aesthetically. This spatial separation helps to ensure that yelling does not occur in the library, that eating occurs in a restaurant and not a museum gallery, and so forth. As urbanist Lewis Mumford observed, the setting should reinforce the activities that occur in it.[4]

Buildings, however, can "learn" from their occupants and surroundings. In *How Buildings Learn: What Happens after They Are Built,* Stewart Brand portrays the life of buildings as they endure and change through several generations.[5] The explosion of electronic uses is now requiring physical settings to accommodate a range of new digital activities and communication patterns. Today, we face the need and the opportunity to create more useful, richer settings throughout the home, the office, and the public places we inhabit. In the following sections, I follow the Drucker dictum, and observe where this future is happening.

THE FLUIDITY OF HOME

In the preindustrial era, the spatial glue holding together work, life, and commerce was strong; formally, the various functions could occur in close proximity to each other. Historian Richard V. Francaviglia profiles the 1875 Perkins House of Athens, Ohio, as a representative example of this close coupling: the drug store and medicine store were located at the corner of the ground floor, while the remainder of the building retained its private residential orientation (see Figure 2.1).[6] Imagine the life events that passed through such settings— work conflicts and collaboration, family intimacies and social encounters, all played out inside a single structure. And beyond that structure, the day-to-day activities of work, commerce, and leisure were tightly bound within a small geographic zone. As sociologist Thomas Bender reported, a great proportion of villagers during the colonial period lived, worked, and died within a few miles of their birthplace.[7]

Over the course of the last century, the *fluidity* of our activities has increased dramatically. With the aid of numerous technological developments— the car, the telephone, and, today, digital communications—we have become increasingly able to bridge the space between widely dispersed places.[8] Concurrent with these advances, there has been a specialization in the types of

Figure 2.1. Colonial home-based workplace, Athens County, Ohio, 1875.

places we build and the locations where we build them. Indeed, the standard process of zoning different parts of a city for different uses reflects and has enabled these trends: residential housing units go in one part of town, commercial buildings in another part, and industrial parks in yet another area. Over time, each zone takes on mass and breadth.[9]

Heralded by visionaries such as Le Corbusier in *The City of To-Morrow and Its Planning* and later attacked by preservationists such as Jane Jacobs in *The Death and Life of Great American Cities,* the notion of separating functions across space became widely advocated shortly after World War II, marked by the rise of the "middle landscape" of suburban dwellings.[10] With respect to setting, the message throughout the second half of the twentieth century remained clear: work and home and shopping were to be separate environments, each with its own design and social circumstances.

FROM THE CAR TO THE WIRE

Traditional settings, however, are being altered by digital technologies, which are fundamentally affecting the longstanding rationale for distinct locations and conventional building types. The spatial fluidness of electronic communication can link activities traditionally separated by physical space. It is important to note that in 1998, for the first time, the number of new businesses started in residential settings exceeded the number of new businesses started in regions specifically zoned for commerce.[11] That statistic illustrates a pervasive phenomenon: work has crept into the home through data and telephone portals. From the occasional e-mail at home and a few workdays at home to part-time home-working, from businesses based at home to "free agent" consultants for whom the home is the office, one form of work or another now demands attention from residential designers.

There are a variety of well-documented reasons why traditional residences are also increasingly places of work. For the entrepreneur, there are obvious cost savings over commercial space as well as the capability to create an electronic storefront for the enterprise through web pages, virtual offices, electronic bulletin boards, and more. The small office/home office ("SoHo") market is emerging as one of the fastest growing markets in the country.[12] And while stories of multimillion-dollar companies begun out of garages in Silicon Valley are legion—the founding of Hewlett-Packard being one highly publicized example—by now the phenomenon has stretched far and away from Silicon Valley.

The number of telecommuters—those who spend at least part of their day working from home—grew from 4 million in 1990 to 15.7 million in 1998, with the Bureau of Labor Statistics reporting the largest gain in wage-and-salary telework.[13] While home-based work will never be the principle location of work for many, one way or another it has become a location for some form of computer-based work or activity. This trend is becoming a significant new force in both office and residential development.[14] Whether it is an employer providing high-bandwidth connectivity to the home, live-work lofts doubling as offices for startups, or masterplanned communities with street-facing home offices, work is reappearing in the home, recalling the days of the Perkins House. But this time, work is aided and abetted by digital and communications technology.

This is not to suggest that home designs are always agile in their adjustments to technology. The traditional elements of the home both convey a range of meanings and contain a range of functions. Consequently, some elements (the fireplace, living room, dining room) may continue to be valued, if only occasionally used, because of their symbolic meaning.[15] But, even with these longstanding symbols intact, technology can have significant impact on the design and use of residential space. This was certainly true for heating (e.g., the furnace) and electricity. These technologies produced such revolutionary forms of heat and light that everyone was effectively freed from the hearth. The television introduced a form of spatial gravity into the home, drawing us into its own new setting, the "TV room." Shelter for the car has replaced the shaded porch as the public entrance to the house and, in many cases, now occupies as much or more square footage as the bedroom (see Figure 2.2).

Figure 2.2. Early carport design.

In comparison to the grand entrance of the automobile into residential design, the computer made a relatively quiet entrance into our homes. Through the study door, the computer found its way to a desk, helping us write the occasional letter, keep track of our spending, or play a new type of game. To date, most digital settings have not evolved beyond the computer's adoptive place of arrival: sharing a surface with pen and pencil holders in some auxiliary corner for part-time use. Many existing homes dedicate some space, where available, for a separate office (see Figure 2.3).

But the increasing convergence of technologies, combined with continuing advances in residential access to high bandwidth, suggest that there are transformative design possibilities for recombining a variety of different digital functions into entirely new residential settings. A recent survey of prospective buyers reveals a sea change in attitudes. Planning for computer use is now a "definite"; some 65 percent of those surveyed believe it should be included in house designs, making it the most appealing new amenity for home buyers (see Figure 2.4).[16]

Figure 2.3. Early computer-study design.

HOME LAYOUTS FOCUS ON OFFICES, GREAT ROOMS

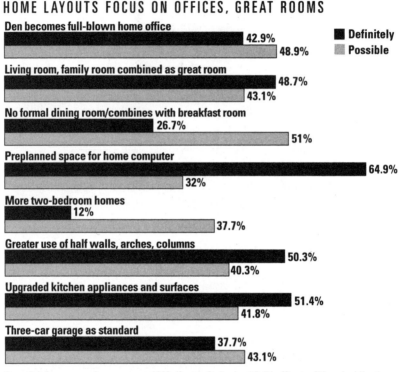

Figure 2.4. Consumer preference survey, 1998. (Source: Professional Builder/Greater Chicagoland Housing Foundation Study)

The incorporation of technology into live-work arrangements is increasingly common in more traditional residential designs, with integrated networks becoming a popular aspect of these designs. According to Steve Raschke of Digital Interiors, a residential wiring company, "next to kitchen counters, [high-speed wiring is] becoming the next most popular upgrade."[17] This market demand is leading major developers around the country to integrate advanced wiring systems into new homes. Masterplanned communities like Celebration in Orlando, Florida, DC Ranch near Scottsdale, Arizona, Ladera Ranch in Irvine, California, and Issaquah Highlands in Washington require builders to follow wiring specifications that ensure high-bandwidth availability throughout development.[18] In some cases, the wiring system is just one amenity among many; in other cases, it is incorporated into an innovative residential design element, such as a prominent and easily accessible home office.

The two most common settings for digital technology use are currently the study and the den. Traditionally, the study would be for concentrated work, and the den would be for passive activities like watching television and chatting. A transformative design project now needs to reconsider the essential functions—first separating public and private activities and then designing recombinations based on new communication and activity patterns. Often the study can be recombined into a more public and at least part-time office, perhaps with a street presence. Such a design option has been enacted in Orenco Station, Oregon, where twenty-four live-work townhouses—all with street-facing business office entrances—line the main boulevard of this traditional neighborhood development (see Figure 2.5).[19] Correspondingly, more private functions can either retain classic elements (e.g., the bedroom)

Figure 2.5. Orenco Station live-work units.

or become flexible space (e.g., the "great room").[20] In this way, the home continues to retain its meaning as a place for relaxation and comfort, while accommodating its additional function as a place of work and productivity.

Several variations of residential redesign of public and private spaces spurred by technology were recently featured in "The Un-Private House," an exhibition at the Museum of Modern Art (MoMA) in New York (see below).[21] As conveyed by the range of design ideas in the MoMA exhibition, digital

---

"UN-PRIVATE HOUSE" EXHIBITION, MUSEUM OF MODERN ART, NEW YORK

A recent exhibit at New York's Museum of Modern Art (MoMA), "The Un-Private House," highlighted an assortment of design changes that digital technologies are causing in the home. Organized around twenty-six different residential designs (most of which have been built), the underlying premise of the show is that the traditional notion of the home as a retreat for private contemplation has been replaced with a more electronically saturated environment. These formulations range from an "always on" Manhattan loft that beams electronic stock-market ticker-tape into every crevasse, to subterranean media rooms that provide electronic entertainment settings in a modernist-inspired Napa Valley retreat.

But, as writer Paula Dietz adroitly notes in her review of the exhibition, "Despite the intrusions of the outside world through glass walls and electronic hookups, people still retain the option of turning off their computers and otherwise retreating—and many of the architects represented in the show have proved adept at helping them do just that."[1] For example, a central feature of the Shorthand House in Houston, Texas, which was designed by architect François de Menil and presented in the MoMA show, is changeable functions of work and living space, such as an enclosed desk that can be opened to reshape an entire room into a home office or closed to create a more informal space (see Figures 2.8, 2.9). Notes de Menil, "Media and technology blur the distinctions between the public and private realms. . . . The Shorthand House reflects this potential for overlapping simultaneity of realms. Traditional rooms are reduced to the components that best accommodate their function and occupancy. These symbols can be joined and related in a variety of combinations, each resulting in a different spatial condition."[2]   ◀◀

1 Paula Dietz, "House Rules: Have They Really Changed As Much As MoMA Thinks," *Metropolis*, October 1999. Available at http://www.metropolismag.com/new/content/oct_99/oc99hr.html.
2 Quoted in the Un-Private House, http://www.moma.org/exhibitions/un-privatehouse/project_18.html.

---

technologies are contributing to recombinations of domestic settings at every scale, from the 900-square-foot urban loft to the 8,000-square-foot wired estate. There are, in fact, exciting new developments in the urban loft market, driven, in part, by the increasing numbers of young professionals and empty nesters who choose to live in the city.[22] The live-work loft trend, which has its origins in SoHo in New York and SoMa in San Francisco, has now taken root in most major cities in North America, from the conversion of old libraries in Back Bay Boston and ballrooms in Brooklyn to warehouses in Detroit and state office buildings in Austin.[23]

A common feature of these designs is to facilitate live-work arrangements, including high-bandwidth connectivity. The lofts include several elements of recombinant design: they retain both functional and architectural meaning; they incorporate new functions taking advantage of spatial fluidity; and facilitate a seamless connection between the physical and electronic environment. A recent example of such recombinant design is the Old Bank redevelopment in downtown Los Angeles. Occupying six abandoned commercial buildings (including a former bank), the project aims to create a dynamic live-work environment featuring 250 lofts. Through high-bandwith connectivity (known as category 5 or "cat-5") the lofts can accommodate almost any live-work arrangement required by the users. A similar adaptive reuse has been done in New Orleans. There, the Cotton Mill redevelopment entailed the rehabilitation and conversion of an abandoned downtown warehouse into approximately 300 apartments and condominiums, all of which are equipped for high-speed Internet access. And, to retain connections to its

COURTESY OF HRI GROUP

Figure 2.6. Past and future: recombinant use of the tower at the Cotton Mill.

Figure 2.7. Culinary lesson in the Digital House.

original use while embracing telecommunications demands, the original water tower was converted into a cellular tower (see Figure 2.6).

The ultimate transformation, many predict, will be when the rise of information appliances creates a *seamless threshold connection* throughout the
home. The "always on" condition of Internet connection (such as high-bandwidth residential connections and internal home networks) will, under this
scenario, continue to evolve until many aspects of domestic activity will weave
in and out of electronic and physical space. The Digital House designed by
architects Hariri & Hariri for *House Beautiful* in 1999 imaginatively captures
this possibility; in it, the kitchen comes complete with an electronic monitor
for obtaining culinary lessons on demand (see Figure 2.7).

THE RECOMBINANT WORKPLACE

As we can see by the electronic migration of work activities into the home,
the information economy is calling into question a fundamental assumption
on which commercial offices are based: the need to assemble talent and materials in one place in order to do business. Today, as businesses invest heav-

ily in intranets (the infrastructure backbone for a flexible, mobile work structure), the fluid nature of where we work appears to be increasing. According to the Gartner Group, an Internet market research group, a large portion of knowledge workers expect access to their systems remotely, and by 2003, one-third of the U.S. workforce will be accessing systems remotely.[24] For this reason, it is not surprising to find corporations investing heavily in remote access capabilities. Some, such as the Ford Motor Company and Delta Airlines, have gone so far as to subsidize home computers and Internet access for their employees.[25, 26]

Current efforts to redesign the work setting seek to address both new technologies and our corresponding new work habits. One theme among new workspace designs is to move away from traditional notions of spatial assignment. In place of the familiar hierarchical allocation of office space—the boss in the corner office, management in perimeter offices, and staff workers in cubicles—there is a growing interest in designing offices to facilitate collaborative, interactive, and remote-location work environments.[27]

In the traditional work setting, individual spaces have taken the form of private offices or desk cubicles. Interactive spaces have taken the form of meeting or conference rooms, while the lunch room, the designated smoking area, and the infamous water cooler (more accurately, the coffee pot) have constituted public spaces. But digital technology (and the corollary rise of the knowledge worker) has disrupted all that, and various approaches have already been taken to recombine the elements.

Recombination is occurring more readily in certain sectors of the business world than in others. Traditionally conservative businesses have made subtle inroads, such as an adaptive change of an office or cube to accommodate personal computers or teamwork. But many advertising and consulting firms, for example, have taken a much more transformative approach to workplace digital place design.[28] Their nascent attempts sought to eliminate paper and rethink issues of privacy. Perhaps the most high-profile example of this bold approach was the New York office of advertising firm Chiat-Day, which was designed by Gaetano Pesce. It provided an extreme and well-publicized example of workplace design that emphasized collective workspaces, with personal effects relegated to small lockers. Similarly ambitious designs for knowledge-intensive firms like Andersen Consulting and Ernst and Young aggressively embraced hotelling, encouraging staff to reserve an office rather than having one permanently, thereby reducing the need for expensive downtown real estate.[29]

Over the last decade, these heavy-handed designs have given way to more integrative recombinations of physical and electronic space—recombinations that balance the fluidity afforded by technology with the more traditional uses of workspace. (Indeed, both the New York and Los Angeles offices of TBMA/Chiat-Day moved to balanced recombinations of space and place in 1998.)[30] For example, in the offices of KPMG, an auditing and consulting company in Silicon Valley, flexible work arrangements are combined with exten-

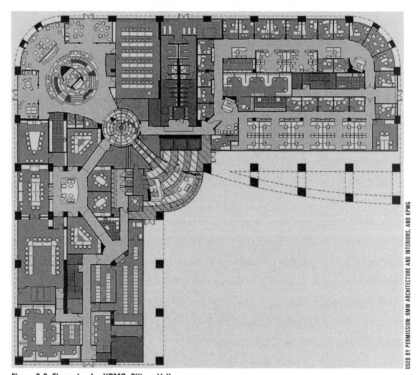

Figure 2.8. Floor plan for KPMG, Silicon Valley.

USED BY PERMISSION: RMW ARCHITECTURE AND INTERIORS, AND KPMG

sive collaboration and meeting space. The floor plan combines communal-style areas toward the center with flexibly assigned workspaces along the axes (see Figure 2.8). The multifunctional elements, combined with the traditional layout along the axes, led architect Michael Brill to observe that, "This traditional layout and feel may offer a reassuring feel of permanence to employees and clients who have had experience with the jittery start-up feel of many Silicon Valley companies."[31] A theme throughout the design is the balancing of innovative collaborative meeting space with more traditional office workspaces.

Designers of "transformative" settings now seem to better appreciate the need for synergy between electronic and physical space.[32] Architect Francis Duffy has documented the movement toward more integrated office designs, and in particular, to what he calls a "club" design. He notes, "Club organizations are for knowledge work, i.e., for office work that transcends data-handling because it can only be done through exercising considerable judgment and intelligence. Typically, work in such organizations is both highly autonomous and highly interactive. The pattern of occupancy tends to be intermittent over an extended working day. A wide variety of time-shared, task-based settings serve both concentrated individuals and group interactive work. Individuals and teams occupy space on an 'as-needed' basis, moving around it to take advantage of a wide range of facilities."[33]

One of the largest implementations of a transformative approach is the 500,000-square-foot Nortel Networks headquarters, recently completed in a converted industrial shell outside of Toronto. Using the city as an organizing metaphor, the project has avenues (hallways) and neighborhoods (sections of the building) that identify the location of office and social spaces. Rather than creating a completely fluid use of space, as Pesce did for Chiat-Day, a sense of "ownership" was important at Nortel, where work groups were able to design and inhabit their own spaces. Formal work areas feature a range of work environments and, just as important, the headquarters features cafés, displays, and informal nodes to promote communication across corporate divisions (see "City Life at Nortel Networks," page 44).[34]

These new designs reaffirm the value of innovative physical workplace design, even though the spatial fluidity afforded by digital technology might

---

CITY LIFE AT NORTEL NETWORKS

Opened in 1997, the Nortel Networks headquarters is based in an old 500,000-square-foot factory in the greater Toronto area. Rather than being a virtual metaphor for electronic space, "the city" serves as a conceptual metaphor at Nortel. Designed by Hellmuth, Obata & Kassabaum (HOK), the layout is organized around various urban landmarks (avenues, parks); workspaces are divided into color-coded neighborhoods that are dotted with murals, cappuccino and sandwich shops, a travel agency, and a full-service bank branch (the reconfigured bank!). As Nortel's Eugene Roman told *Fast Company*, "The city draws people out and creates interactions that wouldn't happen in our buildings."[1] The interactions are further encouraged by Nortel's use of several democratic design principles, such as allowing for employee involvement in the design of a group workspace (see opening photograph).

The interactions are also designed to cross the digital threshold into electronic space, as a related feature of Nortel's workspace is an aggressive telework program that provides comprehensive support for its teleworkers. Nortel has further blurred the functional distinction between home and work with an on-site "test house," called HomeBase, where network options for setting up a home office are physically laid out and an entire division is devoted to supporting the approximately 7,800 Nortel employees worldwide who telework.   ◀◀

1 Lisa Chadderdon, "Nortel Switches Cities," *Fast Company*, August 1998, 112-121.

---

at first blush suggest that space had lost its "stickiness," or ability to evoke activities and meaning over time. To the contrary, the desire of office colleagues to work in teams and to have a physical setting that supports this function has not gone away. Rather, the focus is on the new functional meaning of the workplace: it must facilitate collaborative communication; serve as a headquarters "hub" (physically and electronically) for an increasing array of dispersed activities; and provide a physical and symbolic site for corporate culture, interaction, and creativity.

TOWARD A DIGITAL AESTHETIC

Commercial and mixed-use developments are beginning to incorporate electronic and digital technology into their overall design aesthetic. The former

Figure 2.9. The "Web Wall" at 55 Broad Street.

Drexel Burnham Lambert headquarters in Lower Manhattan is leading the way. The building at 55 Broad Street once symbolized the junk bond-fueled overbuilding of many downtown commercial areas, but is now an icon of the movement toward a digital design aesthetic. Transformed into a "wired" building by the Rudin family, its longtime owner, 55 Broad Street is a hub of Silicon Alley activities. From its "Web Wall" of multiple flickering screens in the main lobby to the "Digital Sandbox" videoconferencing and communal-style meeting rooms on the fourth floor and the fifty-odd high-tech business and educational tenants, the building supplies an overall digital functionality *and* aesthetic that sends a clear signal of its commitment to technology in the workplace (see Figure 2.9).[35]

While perhaps lacking the panache of 55 Broad Street, commercial developments throughout the country are incorporating digital technology as a central feature of their overall design (or redesign) and marketing. The *1997*

Review of the American Institute of Architects Center for Advanced Technology Facilities Design featured some twenty buildings selected by a jury for innovation in the integration of technology into design; the lineup includes commercial office complexes such as the NYNEX Oliver Street Tower in Boston.[36] While none of the selected buildings carries anything like the "Web Wall" of the Rudin building, each contains a sophisticated approach to the functional and aesthetic issues of technology.[37] For example, the NYNEX project adopts a sleek corporate aesthetic, yet retains both flexibility and a commitment to informal public space. As the AIA review states, "The entire circulation path around the building core is designed as public space. The workstations align with the splayed exterior walls creating irregularly shaped 'leftover' spaces at their intersection with circulation. These open spaces contain libraries, computer demonstration and open meeting spaces. They are the dynamic resolution of multiple building geometries and they establish a vibrant 'Main Street' for the twelve floors of the project."[38]

The digital aesthetic is not always pleasing to the eye and it does not always play a dramatic role in positively affecting the urban and suburban

Figure 2.10. Yahoo headquarters.

landscape. A drive around many of the Silicon Valleys, Alleys, and Hills now found throughout the country often reveals a disjointed array of hastily constructed, light-industrial developments catering to start-up companies. In a stinging review of Silicon Valley office designs, Mitchell Schwarzer writes: "If there is a language in the Valley, it is supplied by the sign. Everywhere, the company logos are downloaded onto roadsides appalling in the doldrums of mass-produced uniformity. In place of urbanistic gradations of scale, space, and density are commonplace buildings and streets made special only by their company stars, the emblems of Intel and Apple, a dialect that relates far more to global capital and cyberculture than to local history or public space."[39] There are noteworthy exceptions to these observations (the 3Com campus comes to mind), but Schwarzer's overall conclusion is unavoidable to anyone who has visited Silicon Valley. While the interior designs may represent innovative combinations of physical and electronic settings, the commercial landscape can be uninspiring (see Figure 2.10).

CROSSING THE E-THRESHOLD

For the retail industry, setting appeal has been essential to inspiring impulse shopping. Indeed, the spatial organization of department stores such as Saks Fifth Avenue can most easily be understood by the percent of sales achieved in a given area. High-profit items (e.g., cosmetics) are located front and center with low-profit items (e.g., beauty salon) in the catacombs of the store.[40]

One of the major retail trends of the last decade has been to reduce point-of-sale costs: real estate, operations, overhead, and sales help. By selling basic goods in cheap, stripped-down, warehouselike stores, big-box businesses like Wal-Mart have profited and proliferated around the country. Recently, the dramatic decline in the cost of Internet access coupled with the rise of electronic commerce applications (e-commerce) has begun to lure businesses out of physical settings altogether. The result is a growing electronic bazaar, where seemingly everything is for sale, including music, books, food, games, and computers.

The enthusiasm exhibited by the financial markets for electronic commerce and related dot-com sector companies suggests, at first, the erosion of the value of place in the retail markets.[41] And there are several cases, notably the closing of Egghead Software stores and the opening of Egghead.com, that provide illustrative instances of this trend.[42] A closer look at the industry, however, reveals a more complicated pattern of electronic and physical combinations emerging from the rise of e-commerce.

Digital technologies are dramatically reconfiguring the physical and electronic relationships between point-of-sale, distribution, and production locations. The United Colors of Benetton, for example, offsets its costly retail presence by using digital technology to reduce its inventory and distribution costs.[43] Other operations such as Wal-Mart have used a less "boutique" approach to back-office technology management: consolidating several retail operations—hardware, clothing, autocare—into one retail megaspace supported by a technology-intensive supply-management system.

These developments suggest that the value of physical place is not going away but is evolving in its nature and purpose. Transformative digital place designs have coupled retail space with a marketing function to create an overall buying and branding experience, while a technologically sophisticated supply chain-management system drives down product costs. Slowly, the transformation of physical space from point-of-sale to marketing experience is occurring, with electronic medium switching from a marketing channel (via television) to the point-of-sale channel. We are increasingly buying through the electronic medium (Internet) once used principally for advertising, while, conversely, the physical retail space is increasingly stressing brand experience (marketing). There

PHOTO BY AUTHOR

Figure 2.11. Gap storefront in New York City, 1999.

are several variations on this theme of reversing the point-of-sale and marketing functions across the digital and electronic threshold. Gateway computers provides testing stores (Gateway Country) to support its mail and e-commerce business. Niketown promotes the experience of Nike. Gap stores use valuable front retail windows to advertise online shopping (see Figure 2.11). Levi Strauss uses technology to market and measure jeans.[44]

For some retail businesses, however, this marketing-branding relationship with the consumer is not worth the associated brick-and-mortar costs. The transformation to a completely electronic presence is strongest for those functions least supported by a physical presence. Financial and travel services, for example, have dramatically accelerated their online efforts. Deutsche Banc Alex. Brown estimates online trading will generate $5 billion in annual revenues in 2002. Moreover, online insurance sales are expected to score revenues of $19 billion a year, followed by e-banking and e-payments, with $11.5 billion and $9 billion, respectively.[45]

Local banks are closing around the country, as ATM machines provide convenient and cost-efficient banking services (see "Banking on the Third Place," page 51). Similarly, the era of the local travel agent may be coming to a close, as online travel services—pioneered by reservation services such as Sabre—become the dominant mode for reservations.[46] In many towns, consumer and retail operations like banks and travel agents seem destined to join the drive-in movie theater in the junkyard of outdated enterprises.[47]

COMMERCE@DIGITAL.LATTE

To recall Edward Casey's counterintuitive observation about the enduring power of place in the electronic era, there are now a variety of commercial operations that emphasize the amenity of place as part of the overall retail experience.[48] We are no longer content to go to the corner bookstore with its small inventory of books and scarcity of anything else. Today, the experience needs to be multifaceted—books, music, and, of course, a café. The tremendous success of companies such as Borders and Starbucks is due, in part, to their commodification of Ray Oldenburg's "third place," where informal social exchange can occur. We need to go somewhere to hang out; it

Figure 2.12. Wells Fargo Bank, Claremont, California, 1998.

used to be the barbershop and diner but now it is the cappuccino station and the bookshop superstore.[49] In Claremont, California, for example, where a spacious old bank has been remade into a bank/cappuccino enterprise, the old can be combined with the new to create a new kind of public space (see Figure 2.12).

As the Claremont example shows, local commercial places not only provide economic benefits to their communities, but can serve as "third places." Digital technologies are affecting which places serve this recombination of functions and how they serve it. Recombinations are not just occurring in the use of banks as third places, but almost every place is affected due to the fluidity brought about by the pervasive use of portable and wireless digital technologies. Consequently, cafés around the world retain the value of their places and, at the same time, reestablish themselves in the digital age. Even in Finland, a country that has the highest penetration of cellular phones in the world, they are used quietly in communal spaces. As travel writer Susan Spano recently wrote about Helsinki, "The Atelijee Bar, intimate and stylish, frequented by Finns drinking espresso and whispering into Nokia cell

---

BANKING ON THE THIRD PLACE

When the residents of Pescadero, an agricultural town in California known as "artichoke heaven," were not getting their fresh-baked artichoke herb bread from Norm's market, they could be found doing business or stopping in at the local Bank of America. Like many Main Street banks across the country, Pescadero's Bank of America branch occupied a prominent position in the local neighborhood. As one fourth-generation resident of this working class community of 30,000 told the *Los Angeles Times*, "The bank is such a friendly place that sometimes you just stop in to say hello."[1]

When the Bank of America closed its Pescadero branch after seventy years of service, much more than a physical location for banking was lost. But, according to bank officials, the location was no longer of value, as most, if not all functions could be completed either by ATM or online. While some years later, a smaller bank would reopen in this town, other communities have not been so fortunate: over the last ten years, some 400 banks have closed nationwide. Since 1976, eighty-four banks have closed in California alone. In most towns around the country it is common to find assorted banks for sale or lease as the recombination of the banking industry reveals itself along commercial strips and in other shopping areas.[2] ◀◀

1 Mary Curtius, "Town Discovers It Can't Bank On Its Only Bank," *Los Angeles Times*, 10 April 1997, 1A.
2 For a comprehensive overview of telecommunications changes in the financial industry, see Office of Technology Assessment, "Chapter 5: Technological Change and the Location of Information-Based Service Industries," *The Technological Reshaping of Metropolitan America* (Washington, D.C.: Office of Technology Assessment, September 1995).

---

phones, is one of my favorite places in the city."[50] A sense of place is enjoyed anew, this time with the aid of our wireless companion.

CONCLUSION: FROM PURE TYPES TO COMPLEX SETTINGS

"We shape our buildings and then our buildings shape us," is a famous Churchill phrase. But, the actual chore of tracing the technological, economic, social, and cultural impact on specific design change is a complicated and, at times, speculative enterprise. Terry Smith's *Making the Modern* performs this task mightily, demonstrating how technology, in this case industrial Fordist technology, can come to permeate the architecture, art, and culture of an era.[51] Smith's analysis reveals how the industrial architecture designed by Albert

Kahn for Henry Ford became emblematic of the Modernist era, proclaiming the roles of industry, function, and efficiency to be cultural priorities.

This chapter has sought to uncover clues as to how digital places are emerging at the setting level. Drawing upon these clues and their association to the four strands of recombinant design, the following design features emerge:

■ *Residential Places.* Facilitated by digital technology, the fluidity of work is allowing a closer knitting of home and work environments. New residential designs can accommodate the intensification of work in the home environment by allowing, for example, for more ample and public work settings. This would respect the value of the home as a place of relaxation, and demarcate its new function as a place of production. The den might become a more public multifunction workroom, perhaps replacing the garage as the closest spatial link to neighborhood streets. High-bandwidth wiring throughout the home can facilitate a range of design choices and mark the emergence of the ubiquitous threshold between the home and the electronic environment.

■ *Workplaces.* Spatial fluidity is increasing at work, due in substantial measure to digital technology. Workplaces, however, retain their meaning and value particularly for encouraging quality face-to-face activities. Offices can relinquish standard arrangements in favor of more diversified settings that focus on the functions of concentrated work, small group interaction, and casual interaction. The office can still retain a symbolic importance as the hub of activity, but in a more diversified set of locations, connected, in part, by an increasingly seamless digital threshold, both in terms of software (e.g., business intranet) and hardware (e.g., modem banks).

■ *Retail and Third Places.* While e-commerce will continue to explode in terms of consumer and business-to-business sales, this will not erase the value of accessible retail public places and related opportunities for retail sales, marketing, and street life. The recombination of traditional retail environments can accommodate these needs and provide additional links to the electronic dimension.

Architect Toyo Ito recently proclaimed, "Current building types are moribund. They no longer have the strength to keep up with the realities of society and the huge scale of the digital network ocean."[52] The changes and recombinations highlighted in this chapter demonstrate the strains on traditional building types—office, residential, commercial—as they are adapted to new digitally enabled uses. Still, the overall meaning of type retains heuristic value: we still look to the home as a principal setting for relaxation and domestic life; we look to the workplace, wherever it may be, as the locale of labor; and we still go around the corner, when we are not purchasing online, to browse the latest fruits and fashions.

While virtual and electronic settings are expanding, the role of quality physical settings is not dying, but changing. The retail sector continues to boom, but is stressing more efficient use of space and employing enhanced marketing and entertainment activities. In the housing sector, various trends will make residential design a more important issue, as we increasingly choose to work and entertain at home. And while the workplace is transforming, the notion of place and interaction is not evaporating but shifting to a more complex assortment of possible work and home arrangements as mediated through a range of communication technologies and mediums.

In the final analysis, these new and provocative digital settings cannot fully replace the traditional sensory experience of place. We all recognize that digital technology cannot replicate the experience of being in a classroom, an office, a ballpark, or an exotic vacation spot. These settings cannot be accurately simulated, because direct sensory and interactive experiences are difficult for technology to imitate well. (Real life is still the best high-bandwidth experience!) But digital technology can alter and reshape our world in a manner that provides an increasing number of choices in how and where we experience our day-to-day work and leisure activities.

NOTES

1   Edward Casey, *The Fate of Place: A Philosophical History* (Los Angeles: University of California Press, 1998).

2   Peter F. Drucker, "The Future That Has Already Happened," *Harvard Business Review* (September-October 1997): 20.

3   See Daniel Stokols, "Human Development in the Age of the Internet," in *Assessment of the Environment Across the Lifespan,* S.L. Friedman and T.D. Wachs, eds. (Washington, D.C.: American Psychological Association, 1999).

4   Lewis Mumford, *The City in History: Its Origins, Its Transformations, and Its Prospects* (New York: Harcourt Brace & Company, 1961).

5   Stewart Brand, *How Buildings Learn: What Happens After They Are Built* (New York: Penguin Books, 1994).

6   Richard V. Francaviglia, *Main Street Revisited: Time, Space, and Image Building in Small-Town America* (Iowa City: University of Iowa Press, 1996).

7   Thomas Bender, *Community and Social Change in America* (Baltimore: Johns Hopkins University Press, 1978), 63.

8   For a recent review of the space-place convergence, see Frances Cairncross, *The Death of Distance* (Cambridge: Harvard Business School Press, 1997).

9   See Karen A. Frank and Lynda H. Schneekloth, eds., *Ordering Space: Types in Architecture and Design* (New York: Van Nostrand, 1994).

10 Le Corbusier, *The City of To-Morrow and Its Planning* (Cambridge: MIT Press, 1929; reprinted, 1971); Jane Jacobs, *The Death and Life of Great American Cities* (New York: Random House, 1961); Peter Rowe, *Making a Middle Landscape* (Cambridge: MIT Press, 1991).

11 In 1997, in a reversal of the previous year, more businesses were started at residential than commercial sites; the tally was 705,000 to 610,000. *Inc.,* May 1998, 39. Based on data from U.S. Department of Commerce, 1998.

12 Carol Leonetti Dannhauser, "Who's in the Home Office?" *American Demographics* (June 1999).

13 "Cyberdialogue, Tele-work Survey Results, 1998" (Reported at So-Ho Summit, Carlsbad, California, 1998). Bureau of Labor Statistics, 1997.

14 The 1997 FIND/SVP American Internet Users Survey (New York: FIND/SVP) found a nearly 30 percent increase in telecommuting in the United States, from 8.1 million in 1995 to 11.1 million in 1997. The study further estimates that approximately 14 million people will be telecommuting in 2000.

15 See Witold Rybczynski, *Home: A Short History of an Idea* (New York: Penguin, 1987).

16 "Annual Customer Survey, 1998" (Conducted for Professional Builders, www.professionalbuilders.com).

17 Comments made by Steve Raschke of Digital Interiors at Digital Communities Briefing, Santa Clara, California, June 25, 1998. In-home wiring (and wireless) sales support the point. Home networking equipment sales are expected to climb to more than $1 billion by 2002, according to Forrester Research. *Interactive Weekly* online, 16 June 1999.

18 Urban Land Institute, *Trends in Master Planned Communities* (Washington, D.C.: Urban Land Institute, 1998).

19 Information on Orenco Station is available at: www.orencostation.com.

20 For a review of these options, see Jennifer Magee, "Home as an Alternative Workplace: Assessing the Environmental and Sociological Design Needs of Full-Time Homeworkers" (Masters thesis, University of Cincinnati, 1998).

21 Terrence Riley, *The Un-Private House* (New York: the Museum of Modern Art, 1999).

22 Karen Frank and Sherry Ahrentzen, *New Households, New Housing* (New York: Van Nostrand Reinhold, 1989); Cheryl Russell, *Americans and Their Homes* (Ithaca, NY: New Strategist Publications, 1998).

23 See http://www.loftsonline.com for a listing of lofts in major U.S., Canadian, and European cities.

24 Cherry Rose Anderson, Gartner Analyst, cited in IDG *Computerworld,* April 1999. For example, according to IDG, 10.1 million remote access concentrator ports were shipped worldwide in 1998 and close to 30 million ports are projected to ship in 2003 (cited in Manish Matta, "Remote Access Market Trends," *The Edge,* Summer 1999, http://www.3com.com/solutions/svprovider/the_edge/1999_03/.

25 David Hamilton and Martha Brannigan, "Fledgling PeoplePC Lands Deals with Ford and Delta," *Wall Street Journal,* 7 February 2000, interactive edition.

26 Kiran Narsu, "Remote Possibilities," *CIO Enterprise,* 15 June 1999.

27 Marilyn S. Zelinsky, *New Workplaces for New Workstyles* (New York: McGraw-Hill, 1998).

28 See Franklin Becker et al., *Worksmart* (Denver: Center for the New West, 1996).

29 Zelinsky, *New Workplaces for New Workstyles.*

30 Warren Berger, "Lost in Space," *Wired Magazine,* February 1999.

31 Michael Brill, "A Space Odyssey," *Metropolis,* November 1998.

32 Those that have taken more transformative approaches have been fairly well profiled in books such as *The New Office, New Workplaces for New Workstyles,* and *Intelligent Spaces: Architecture for the Information Age.* They include Chiat-Day, Andersen Consulting, and about a dozen others that have been frequently mentioned in the literature on new work design.

33 See Francis Duffy, *The New Office* (London: Conran Octopus, 1997).

34 Lisa Chadderdon, "Nortel Switches Cities," *Fast Company,* August 1998. Available at: http://www.fastcompany.com/online/16/nortel.html.

35 See www.55BroadSt.com.

36 American Institute of Architects, *1997 Review of the American Institute of Architects Center for Advanced Technology Facilities Design,* published electronically at http://www.e-architect.com/conted/advntech/CONTENTS.asp.

37 See http://www.e-architect.com/home.asp.

38 American Institute of Architects, *1997 Review of the American Institute of Architects Center for Advanced Technology Facilities Design,* http://www.e-architect.com/conted/advntech/PROJCTS/PROJ6.html.

39 Mitchell Schwarzer, "Beyond the Valley of Silicon Architecture," *Harvard Design Magazine* (Winter/Spring 1999).

40 Jennifer Steinhauer, "The Money Department," in *New York Times Magazine,* 6 April 1997, 62-64.

41 Where once e-commerce was considered the wistful dream of cyber-enthusiasts, it has since become a mainstream economic force and the darling of financial markets. As of 1998, the U.S. Internet economy (revenue from web sales combined with investment in creating and maintaining Internet sales presence) reached $124 billion, with hard goods manufacturers, communications/media businesses, banking services, process manufacturing, and retail as the dominant industries. With forecasts for a $518 billion U.S. Internet economy by the year 2002, the challenge of designing a profitable and adaptable model for the new digital selling floor looms large.

42 Egghead software company functioned as a retail business for fourteen years (1984-98), until it began to lose business to e-commerce providers. To enhance its competitiveness, it closed all of its retail stores, to reemerge as an e-commerce business.

43 "Benetton Tech; Clothing Manufacturer Benetton Expands Its Business through the Use of Advanced Technology," *CNBC News Transcripts,* 8 March 1997.

44 See Paul Goldberger, "The Store Strikes Back," *New York Times Magazine,* 6 April 1997, 45-49.

45 Eileen Buckley, "The Green Revolution: Internet finance is finally set to boom, and players online and off are jockeying for a piece of the action," *The Standard,* May 8, 2000. Available at: http://www.thestandard.com/article/display/1,1151,14678,00.html.

46 Robert Crandall, the late Chairman and CEO of American Airlines, reportedly once remarked that if he had to choose between the airlines and the reservation system as a business, he would choose the reservation system as more profitable. It was a prophetic statement. Cited in Mark Wilson, "The Electronic Impact on Travel Industry" (Paper delivered at the American Association of Geographers, Honolulu, Hawaii, 1999).

47 B. Tedeschi, "For a Personal Touch, Some Sites Add Real People," *New York Times,* 28 June 1999, e-commerce report.

48 Edward Casey, *The Fate of Place* (Los Angeles: University of California Press, 1998), 16.

49 The CEO of Starbucks, Howard Schultz, has adopted the language of sociologist Ray Oldenburg, emphasizing the "third place" attributes of Starbucks. See Howard Schultz interview, *Far East Economic Review,* 18 May 2000, electronic edition. Available at: http://www.feer.com/_0005_18/p44innov.html.

50 Susan Spano, "High Season For Helsinki," *Los Angeles Times,* 27 June 1999, L-1, L-12.

51 Terry Smith, *Making the Modern: Industry, Art, and Design in America* (Chicago: University of Chicago Press, 1993).

52 Cited in Otto Riewoldt, *Intelligent Spaces: Architecture for the Information Age* (London: Laurence King, 1997), 11.

Community and Place: Web-raising event, Los Angeles, 1998.

CHAPTER 3

DESIGNING DIGITAL COMMUNITIES

I N HIS FINAL State of the Union address, President William Jefferson Clinton remarked on the meaning of opportunity in the electronic era: "Opportunity for all requires something else today—having access to a computer and knowing how to use it. That means we must close the digital divide between those who've got the tools and those who don't. Connecting classrooms and libraries to the Internet is crucial."[1] And, indeed, his administration strongly supported the deployment of electronic infrastructures through a host of federally funded initiatives and technical assistance programs.[2]

Two centuries earlier, the "other" Jefferson contemplated the role of education, opportunity, and community within the context of a physical design: the master plan for the University of Virginia. Classical in style, the design was based on an understanding of architecture as a facilitator of discourse and community. Functionally and symbolically, the quad was the organizing feature of the heart of the campus. Distinct pavilions housing each academic department turned their formal pediments inward to face each other, joined together by a continuous colonnade across the central grassy quad. In a brilliant gesture,

Thomas Jefferson closed the top end of the quad with the university library and left the fourth side open to the Virginia hills, which fall away in the distance, establishing a unified academic community open to the people.

These two contributions from U.S. presidents represent radically different but equally important types of community-building efforts. Digital place design at the community level is concerned with developing electronic space in a manner that aids and is abetted by more traditional public places, with widespread access a top priority.

Indeed, from the Campo di Siena in Italy to the Campo de Snoopy at the Mall of America in Minnesota, physical design has been used to symbolize and facilitate community.[3] The central premise of these public spaces is

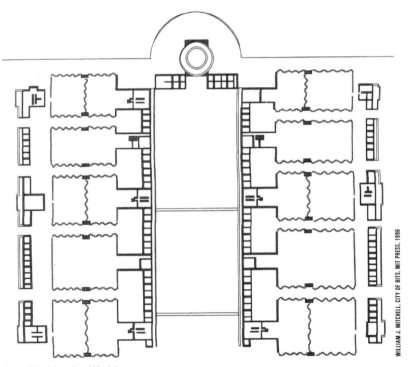

Figure 3.1. University of Virginia.

WILLIAM J. MITCHELL, CITY OF BITS, MIT PRESS, 1996

that the built environment can play an enabling role in creating a sense of community. Enduring interest in free spaces stems from a long tradition of their relationship to the basic ebb and flow of contemporary democracy. As articulated by Sara Evans and Harry Boyte in their book *Free Spaces,* "Put simply, free spaces are settings between private lives and large-scale institutions where ordinary citizens can act with dignity, independence, and vision."[4] Harvard design professor Peter Rowe echoes this sentiment: "Many publicly accessible spaces can have and should have a civic orientation that is direct, palpable, and there for the purposes of reminding us both of who we are and who we might become."[5]

Public institutions play a pivotal role in defining these public spaces, often serving as the location or catalyst for their development. In grand cities such as Washington, D.C., and Paris, monuments and boulevards serve this catalyzing function. In many small cities and towns, public libraries, schools, museums, and community centers function as "anchoring institutions," with their auditoriums, seminar rooms, courtyards, plazas, and gardens—all critical to the creation of community space.[6]

This chapter traces how the strands of recombinant design can affect the evolution of the public realm. How does the rise of electronic communities affect the traditional role and meaning of our civic institutions? Can the fluidity enabled by electronic networks assist in overcoming spatial barriers that often diminish the effectiveness of community institutions? What new and creative threshold connections are possible for sharing local culture and knowledge? What role do public spaces play in providing access to electronic networks? Answers to these questions will provide additional clues as to how digital technologies can influence the recombination of civic and public institutions.

COMMUNITIES OF PLACE AND INTEREST

Successful digital places at the community level are the result of a healthy appreciation for the interaction between communities of place and communities of interest.[7] Communities of place bind people together through their associations with a particular location: a group of people meet on a local school board, serve on a local commission, hang out together at a café, visit a cultural attraction, or attend a community event.

Communities of interest transcend specific locations. People form such communities around a common interest, such as politics or art or parenting issues. Such communities may or may not be linked to a place (a local chapter); their distinguishing feature is that they do not require a physical location to exist. Community activities—sharing information about programs and developments, interacting at various social and professional levels, and networking and sponsoring events—can take place though electronic means (e.g., the Internet) independent of a fixed place.

The key to building vibrant digital communities is to understand the differences and intersections between communities of place and communities of interest. It is instructive to recall that Tim Berners-Lee developed the protocols for the World Wide Web in part to emulate the casual interaction he missed when he and his colleagues were not working together at CERN, the European Particle Physics Laboratory in Geneva, Switzerland.[8] In keeping with this original vision, digital communities, when thoughtfully designed, can embody the desirable attributes of both community forms: close affiliation and involvement with a physical place and seamless participation in broader communities of interest.

TRANSFORMING LOST SPACES INTO DIGITAL PLACES

The concern here is with the "civic layer," a component of the public realm that has, in the eyes of many, declined in terms of both its physical representation and its social value.[9] There have been several major studies on the changing nature of civic engagement and public space. Kenneth Gergen in the *Saturated Self* introduces the decline of civic space with a simple story.[10] During the summer, his in-laws used to sit out front and casually interact with their neighbors in a suburb of Minneapolis. With the onset of radio and then television, they moved their summer affairs into the house, slowly losing contact with their neighbors and foregoing the casual, communal interaction that had defined, for them, summer evenings in Minnesota. Functionally, a highly effective, informal civic space became dormant, even if its physical stage, the front porch, remained in place. Moreover, technology had, in this case, increased the appeal of private space and decreased public interaction.

The recent release of *Bowling Alone* by Robert Putnam provides extensive documentation of this decline in civic engagement. For him, the ultimate symbol of decline is not the lawns of Minnesota but the bowling alleys of Connecticut, or more precisely, the Holiday Bowling Lanes in New London. He observes, "Mounted above each lane is a giant television screen displaying the evening's TV fare. Even on a full night of league play team members are no longer in lively conversation with one another about the day's events, public and private. Instead each stares silently at the screen while awaiting his or her turn. Even while bowling together, they are watching alone."[11]

New technologies also threaten to consign formal civic places to marginal status in the life of communities—unused physically and unimportant symbolically. As sociologist Barry Wellman observes, "Suburban shopping malls have become residual agoras, with most social interaction retreating from public spaces to the heretofore private domain of the home." He goes on to note that in his home city of Toronto, "people watch videos at home an average of thirty times per year but go out for entertainment only three or four times a year. The telephone number for Toronto's largest pizza delivery service has become so well known that Canadian immigration officers use it as a test to see if border crossers are bona fide Canadian residents."[12]

The Toronto anecdote is representative of a widespread condition: our electronic experiences appear to be flourishing while communities of place seem to be withering on the vine. The objective of designing digital communities is to connect, where possible, the electronic realm with communities of place. Our classic public institutions—the library, the school, the museum, the community center—can be assessed in order to understand the changing role of these institutions in connecting local communities. While no one civic institution can metamorphose a community into a digital place, each can contribute in a different fashion, as suggested by the strands of recombinant design: fluid spaces for learning, meaningful places for cultural exchange, provocative new aesthetics that connect interests and place, and innovative mechanisms for civic involvement.

THE "HALLOWED" LIBRARY

The threat to meaningful civic space can be illustrated by considering the status of the traditional library. From the first library in Alexandria, Egypt, to the great libraries in the United States built by Andrew Carnegie, the premise was the same: the learner came to the resource, a library building that constituted a cultural and scientific archive.[13] Now, however, the Internet has developed into a resource of information; personal computers and modems have brought many aspects of the traditional library to the learner. And over the last two decades, many of the 9,000 libraries in this country have fallen on rather difficult times.

The lower costs of books, the expansion of bookstore chains, and budget cutbacks in local government have all contributed to the decline in financial and constituent support for local libraries. Given these trends, few were surprised when the Los Angeles County library system filed for bankruptcy in 1995.[14] Recent surveys document similarly dire circumstances on a national level.[15] The Benton Foundation, a technology public-interest group, issued a report, *Buildings, Books, and Bytes,* in 1996 that concluded: "Libraries have their work cut out for them if they do not want to reside on the margins of the revolutionary new digital information market place."[16] Driving such warnings is the perception that these institutions are no longer engaged in a contemporary range of activities. Some observers, watching branch after branch library close, have even been moved to call them "museums of lost technology."[17]

Early attempts by cyber-enthusiasts at "virtual libraries" were noble, if at times naive attempts to make the resources of physical libraries available through the Internet (see Figure 3.2).[18] These nascent approaches were soon overtaken by explosive growth in the commercial dot-com arena, in particular, Amazon.com's position as the electronic bookstore of choice among those in search of literary material—at least, commercially

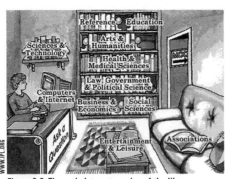

Figure 3.2. The early Internet version of the library.

viable literary material. Claiming over 1 million books in stock, book sales at Amazon reached $610 million in 1998, an astounding increase from 1997 sales of $147.8 million.[19] And in the physical realm, well-located book superstores, such as Barnes & Noble and Borders, have become an often more accessible alternative to libraries for browsing current publications.

RECLAIMING CIVIC SPACE

Success in the private market raises legitimate questions about the value of the public library's presence as a component of the civic layer, and fuels the possibility of its reemergence—with digital technology—as a new form of civic and research institution. Indeed, libraries in several cities are reemerging as vibrant digital civic places. Combining the historical function of the library as a centralized, public repository of literary materials with new capacity to serve as an access point to the world of digital information, a number of major new city libraries have managed to establish vital communities of place by connecting to digital communities of interest.[20]

Nowhere has this recombination—and the concomitant tradeoffs—been more visible than in the construction of the New Main Library in San Francisco (see "The New Main Library, San Francisco," page 66). Since its opening in 1996, critics have noted how the library has grappled with the challenge of achieving its dual mission of a traditional research library and a more informal, accessible source of electronic information for the entire community. With its community rooms, Internet stations, and research locations, the library has provided ample community and online access, though a postoccupancy evaluation of the building found that too little planning was devoted in the design phase to traditional functions such as storage and retrieval of books.[21] Consequently, several million dollars must now be devoted to bringing the traditional activities of the library in line with its more innovative features.

While critiques like the one by Nicholson Baker in *The New Yorker* helped propel the San Francisco library into the national spotlight, the New Main Library is by no means unique in its attempt to link physical and electronic space. Variations of this new recombinant use of libraries have been completed or are underway in cities across North America, including San

Diego, New York, Salt Lake City, Phoenix, Denver, Seattle, and Vancouver. William Walker, director of Research Libraries for the New York City system, reflects the general sentiment toward change: "It's really rather frightening to think of making this transition so quickly. Three years ago, we couldn't imagine the capabilities the World Wide Web brings to the average citizen. [Now] we're helping to level the playing field for the average person who might not get the chance to explore the massive resources available for research."[22]

The stylistic approach to recombinant library environments can vary quite dramatically. Moshe Safdie's Vancouver Library Square, for example, pre-

---

THE NEW MAIN LIBRARY, SAN FRANCISCO

Opened in 1996 at a cost of $140 million, the New Main was hailed as a model for the new century. With its community orientation and technologically sophisticated design, the building was designed to be the city's real and virtual community center, as well as an access point for communication to other communities in the region and around the globe.[1] Through the library's universal cabling system, custom-designed workstations and reading tables are wired into the online public catalog, local area networks, and the Internet at designated terminals.[2]

Designed by architects James Freed of Pei Cobb Freed & Partners and Cathy Simon of Simon Martin-Vegue Winkelstein & Moris, the apportionment of space for public, community, and technology uses has not been without controversy. The new building doubles the book storage capacity of its predecessor, but extensive space dedicated to community groups, media use, and Internet communication has precluded storage needed for up to 200,000 books; increased patronage credited to the library's many amenities and resources has contributed to a spiraling budget deficit.[3] The debate over the library's priorities spread as far as the national press, playing out most prominently in the competing views of two visible figures, Kenneth Dowlin, former chief librarian at the New Main, and Nicholson Baker, who wrote about the library for *The New Yorker* and other publications. Dowlin has said that "The building is designed to bring people into contact with each other as much as with librarians, information, and knowledge."[4] Baker has countered, "The larger the percentage of the pie-chart allotted to cables, data-switches, and leased telecommunications links—to all the chronically costly forms of remote access—the smaller the slice devoted to on-site books, book-repair, shelves, and to the all-important cataloging and reference

---

sents a classic public setting, equipped with a variety of high-tech amenities (see Figure 3.3).[23] Drawing inspiration from the Roman Coliseum, the Library Square project mixes traditional public library functions with both electronic and public space objectives. Physically, the coliseumlike library structure is placed adjacent to an airy, open streetlike promenade, viewable from the extensively glazed building. The library is equipped with electronic access terminals, included in several stations specifically reserved for accessing the local community network.[24] A vertical fiber-optic backbone provides the infrastructure for connection to the electronic world, while the promenade and adjacent open-air stairway provides a physical backbone for open-ended space.

---

staff necessary to make sense of the library's holdings to the general public."[5] *Architecture* magazine took the middle ground: "Computers are as important as books in San Francisco's New Main."[6]

The gaps between the promise of an information-age library and the reality of several design limitations have become all too apparent since the library opened.[7] A 1999 post-occupancy evaluation summarizes the situation: "The library, while designed to be a grand public space, does not function as effectively as it should or as effectively as peer institutions do in several major aspects."[8] The report went on to identify over $10 million in changes that are needed to better accommodate the physical collection and to improve the library's day-to-day operation. While lessons from this path-breaking building are still being distilled, one element is clear: new library designs, developed with the input of staff and patrons, must balance competing demands for electronic and physical collections.[9] ◄◄

1 Kenneth E. Dowlin and Eleanor Shapiro, "The Future of Major Public Libraries," *Daedalus* 125, no. 4 (Fall 1996): 175.
2 See http://www.kron.com/nc4/special/4-3-96/library.html.
3 Susan Byrnes, "A Tale of Two Libraries Offers Lessons for Seattle," *Seattle Times,* 23 February 1998. Available at http://seattletimes.nwsource.com/news/local/html98/libe_022398.html.
4 Kenneth E. Dowlin and Eleanor Shapiro, "The Future of Major Public Libraries," *Daedalus* 125, no. 4 (Fall 1996): 175.
5 Nicholson Baker, "On My Mind," *American Libraries* 30, no. 3 (March 1999): 35.
6 "Wiring the Library," *Architecture,* July 1996, 110.
7 Edward Epstein, "Throwing the Book at Library Study Says S.F. Main Branch Lacks Shelf Space, Has Confusing Layout," *San Francisco Chronicle,* 27 August 1999. Available at http://www.sfgate.com/cgi-bin/article.cgi?file=/chronicle/archive/1999/08/27/MN8913.DTL.
8 Cynthia Ripley, *San Francisco Public Library Post-Occupancy Evaluation Final Report* (San Francisco: City of San Francisco, 4 January 2000).
9 See Byrnes, "A Tale of Two Libraries Offers Lessons for Seattle." John Berry III, "The Key Lesson From San Francisco," *Library Journal Digital* (15 September 1999), http://www.ljdigital.com/articles/views/editorial/19990915_5077.asp, 15 September 1999.

In contrast, Rem Koolhaas's design for the Seattle public library (scheduled to open in 2003) draws upon virtual architecture to arrange both physical and electronic materials. For example, the library has been designed to house books along a spiraling spine of the building, providing easy access after consulting the electronic card catalog. Multimedia technologies will occupy flexible in-floor spaces, as it is expected that these technologies will continue to evolve.[25] Other design approaches to combine and recombine physical and electronic elements will undoubtedly be undertaken by public libraries throughout cities in North America.

SCHOOLS: GROUNDING FLUIDITY

While several major urban libraries have seemingly escaped obsolescence, there is no escaping the reality that spatial fluidity afforded by technology dramatically affects the geographic range over which we can conduct many of our day-to-day activities. As noted in Chapter 1, the challenge of the *fluid lo-*

Figure 3.3. Vancouver Library Square.

cations strand of recombinant design is to recognize this mobility, yet provide grounding physical designs that facilitate multiple forms of communication, both face-to-face and remote (synchronous and asynchronous). New forms of communications have provided unparalleled spatial fluidity in how we conduct our lives. Consequently, the key—and challenge—to *fluid locations* as a recombinant design construct is to harness the power of this fluidity in achieving the overarching goals of a civic enterprise. Local educational institutions provide a site for this challenge.

As early as 1994, 80 percent of community colleges in the United States already offered some form of remote education program, and the numbers have been growing explosively.[26] Gone are the forty-dollar "Learn Spanish in 30 Days" audio tape sets, displaced by new combinations of live, interactive teaching via microcomputers, the Internet, and the World Wide Web. These trends have led Peter Drucker, among others, to pronounce what in his view is an "irrevocable trend," the traditional brick-and-mortar-based university as a moribund institution.[27]

There is no denying the pervasive impact that online and distance learning has had on the educational landscape. But does this suggest that the physical connection between education and student is obsolete? A recent review sponsored by the U.S. Department of Education documented two decades' worth of efforts to promote technology in education and concluded that for grades K-12 the opposite was true: researchers and practitioners had only begun to explore the ability of new Internet-based technologies to "help schools establish stronger connections with students' homes and with the local community . . . and to increase communication and alignment among major social institutions that influence children's overall development." The authors provide several promising examples of Internet use to connect schools and children's activities to the home, community, and larger network of peers.[28]

For example, in Union City, New Jersey, a collaborative public-private partnership has been established to implement a high-speed voice, video, and data network as part of an integrated set of educational reforms. As noted in its report to the National Science Foundation, this urban school district has not only implemented a wide array of digital technological solutions in the classroom, but also done so in a manner that has included both the teachers and the parents in the educational enterprise.[29]

Local schools are becoming "points of presence" for educational digital places in the community. In terms of physical design, the Central Tree Middle School in Rutland, Massachusetts, exemplifies the use of technology that connects with curriculum and community objectives. The resource center and computer lab are located squarely in the center of the ground floor, providing both the focus for project-based local-synchronous learning and an after-hours community resource. In this sense, the center and lab have become as important as the next largest usage—the gymnasium—serving as a forum for student and community interaction (see Figure 3.4).[30]

The wiring of schools is also reconfiguring the spatial relationships between the community of learners and the places where learning occurs. In communities like Issaquah Highlands, Washington, what technology observer George Gilder dubbed the "Issaquah Miracle" has occurred: the community became wired through the efforts of local citizens—in this case parents and kids—to build and maintain their own education network system on behalf of the school system.[31] In this case, Mike Bookey, a local parent, walked into his daughter's classroom and later remarked, "There was only one single telephone line into each classroom. I thought to myself, Is this the way we are going to teach our kids to run the electronic world we were building?" He soon set about leading an effort to build a robust community network that linked to high-bandwidth connections throughout the schools in the local district—a network that was planned and installed while the bureaucracy debated what aspect of the system could and could not be justified as a capital improvement.[32] Issaquah is one of several places throughout the country to base its community network in the education sector, often an electronic cornerstone to local civic infrastructure; in the Issaquah, the computer network is largely run by the next generation of leaders and hackers—known as the "TIPsters" (for technology information project). [33, 34]

At the university level, there has been a strong effort to overcome the physical confines of the university campus by providing a range of distance-learning opportunities. While several new universities (e.g., Western Gover-

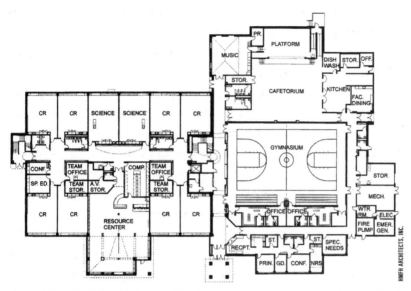

Figure 3.4. Floor plan for Central Tree Middle School.

nors University) and many existing universities offer courses or concentrations through the Internet, this should not be mistaken as defeating the Jeffersonian notion of the university as a place-based campus for the democratic sharing of knowledge and ideas. One can look to the land grant universities, for example, to see how digital technology can be used to enhance community outreach by the educational establishment. Given the rural environment of many land grant universities, one critical area is in providing accessible health care training throughout the state. At the University of Nebraska, the nursing program in rural Kearney is linked to the facilities at the University of Nebraska in Omaha through videoconferencing programs.

In a similar vein, the University of Vermont's Fletcher Allen Telemedicine Outreach Program serves sites throughout rural Vermont and New York, with educational exchanges as far as Vietnam. Recent reviews of the Vermont program provide vivid examples of the value of this access across space, from the ability of local physicians to discuss emergency situations in real time to the ability to make remote diagnoses of patient conditions, thereby saving long, stressful, and costly commutes into the central hospital in Burlington.[35, 36]

COMMUNITY NETWORKS GET REAL

As education and telemedicine initiatives reveal, digital technology networks can link important electronic resources to physical communities. Beyond these formal uses, community networks can also serve to provide an informal forum for communities of interest and their manifestations in communities of place. Beginning with the Well, a community network pioneer started in San Francisco in 1985, the history of "virtual communities" has been a history of communities of interest. Inspired by its 2,000 active users, who participated in a swirl of humanistic philosophy, various offshoots, such as the Electronic Frontier Foundation,[37] were founded by visitors to and participants in the Well.[38] In the ensuing decade, community networks have gone mainstream. Now almost every portal (e.g., Yahoo), major newspaper (e.g.,

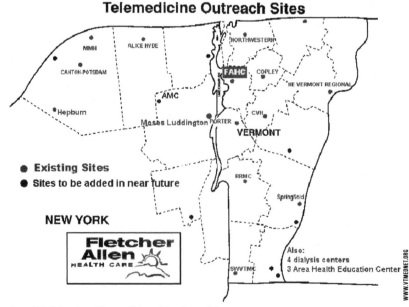

Figure 3.5. University of Vermont Telemedicine Outreach Program.

New York Times), and network news site (e.g., MSNBC) has a discussion and chat component. Even stock market "day-traders" find time to engage in streams of banter about the latest movement in a stock's price.

Community networks like Yahoo's GeoCities and iVillage (an online information and support group for women) are classic communities of interest: they have no necessary connection with any community of place. As illustrated by a web page from iVillage (see Figure 3.6), "channels" are on areas of interest among the community of interest—parenting, careers, and the like.

But a host of "Smart Community" projects, which use wide area and local area networks to support local neighborhood activities, have gone a step further, confirming the potential of linking a digital community of interest to a real place. In Blacksburg, Virginia, Davis and Santa Monica, California, and Blue Sky, Montana, networks provide a robust set of connections among community residents, allowing ongoing interactive communication about local community issues.[39] These networks provide easy access for residents, com-

Figure 3.6. iVillage.com, a "community of interest."

Figure 3.7. Blacksburg, Virginia, discussion page.

munity bulletin boards for local events, and chat rooms and discussion pages for sharing information (see Figure 3.7). Recent evaluations confirm that the important role these community networks play is providing an accessible network for local communities.[40]

Recently, the real estate development sector has become active in developing community networks, specifically for masterplanned communities. The advantage of these communities, most of which are large-scale developments of 1,000 or more acres, is that they can build high-speed community networks from the ground up. Disney's masterplanned development, Celebration, has a community network, as do more recent communities like DC Ranch in Arizona (see "Masterplanned E-Communities," page 76), Summerlin in Las Vegas, Playa Vista in Los Angeles, and Ladera Ranch in Orange County, California.

A common network design among these communities is one that links various uses—education, health care, culture, community postings, governance—to a high-speed network with ubiquitous connectivity across the community. A second common feature is that they are created in a manner that strengthens the local community—through links to schools, hospitals, city halls—while simultaneously providing high-speed Internet access. The rapid growth of masterplanned community networks in the United States suggests that they are quickly becoming a valued amenity, though the extent to which they actually help build community will be an ongoing challenge to residents.

In the meantime, promising results are arriving from Europe, where the Microsoft Corporation has completed trials in London to introduce a local network to twenty-three homes in a local borough (see Figure 3.8). Warmly received by residents, the network has apparently increased discussions of street life. As one resident told a *New York Times* reporter, the new system "has meant that when we meet face to face we can carry on discussions instead of blandly talking about the weather."[41]

AT THE ELECTRONIC COMMUNITY POOL

Not everyone can afford to live in a fancy masterplanned or other amenity-heavy community, which is precisely why nonprofits have been active in creating easily accessible community networks. Returning to the notion of traditional

Figure 3.8. Bits meet bricks on a street in London.

MASTERPLANNED E-COMMUNITIES

Community networks are emerging as an important amenity for masterplanned communities.[1] Disney's Celebration in Orlando was one of the first such communities to include technology as a cornerstone of its development, and this led to the need to establish a means for residents to communicate with each other. Early versions of electronic networks such as Celebration's, which was developed in the 1990s, focused on providing basic community information, bulletin boards, events scheduling, and (rather low-speed) dial-up Internet access.[2]

Subsequent generations of community networks have expanded on these concepts and offerings, with higher-bandwidth access and more diverse applications in education, health, and recreation. "Ranchnet" in the DC Ranch in Arizona, for example, is a state-of-the-art network. Technically, it employs converged voice, video, and data systems, thereby eliminating the need for parallel and redundant telephone, cable, and Internet solutions.[3] From the community network perspective, Ranchnet offers a diverse range of lifestyle (e.g., gourmet cooking) and community (e.g., sports league) pages, many featuring locally written content. Moreover, the residents can "sign up" for certain interest areas, thereby becoming a part of a community of interest located in a community of place.[4] Brent Harrington of DMB Developers, the firm that developed DC Ranch, observes that "the real challenge is not constructing the intranet but getting the community to take ownership over it in terms of content and communication."[5] The general lesson is clear: while developers can create an electronic infrastructure to support community activities, they cannot create community. Community is not a commodity to be purchased but a satisfying result to be achieved.[6] ◀◀

1 See William Clark, "Implications of New Technologies," in *Trends and Innovations in Master Planned Communities* (Washington, D.C.: Urban Land Institute, October 1998).
2 For a recent summary of Celebration's technology approach and history, see Steve Cisler, "Letter from a Community Networker: Celebration, Florida," *First Monday* 4, no. 11 (November 1999). Available at http://www.firstmonday.dk/issues/issue4_11/cisler/index.html; Also: Nancy Wellons, "Live Via Computer," *Orlando Sentinal*, 4 June 2000, 8-16.
3 For an overview of Ranchnet, see http://www.dcranch.com/community/ranchnet.html. For more information on technical dimensions, see Lucent Technologies, "DC Ranch Residents Bring Tomorrow's Technologies Closer to the Home with Lucent Technologies' Homestar Wiring System," Press release, 12 November 1997. Available at: http://www.lucent.com/press/1197/971112.nsa.html. Also: "A Simpler Life in Complicated Times," *Fortune*, 25 May 1998.
4 See Charles Homes, "Wired Community Uses Network to Bring Neighbors Together," *Cox Newspapers*, 26 March 2000. Available at http://www.coxnews.com/washingtonbureau/staff/holmes/COXWIREDCITYADV26.html.
5 Brent Harrington, personal interview, 28 January 2000.
6 Michael Pollan, in his observation about Celebration, suggests communities could be "a commodity—something people buy and consume rather than produce, an amenity rather than an achievement." Michael Pollan, "Town-Building Is No Mickey Mouse Operation," *New York Times Magazine*, 14 December 1997, 60.

"anchoring" institutions, community centers play an important role in realizing *democratic designs*—places that facilitate access through digital technology to the resources available. Recently, many of these community centers have stepped forward to fill the "digital divide," providing computer and Internet access to residents who otherwise would not be able to participate in online community activities. There are approximately 150 such centers around the country, and they are for the most part sponsored by local nonprofit groups. Several studies confirm the importance of these forums in filling a gap: they provide crucial early access to computers and training for jobs in computer-related industries.[42] For the unemployed, public institutions like libraries and community centers provide the tools to search the Web for jobs.[43]

A model for the transformative community center is the PUENTE Learning Center in Los Angeles (see "PUENTE Learning Center," page 78). Every day the center is packed with local residents, many of whom are recent immigrants from Mexico and South America. Some practice administrative skills in staged office environments, complete with supervisor stations and standard business software. Others take English language courses from a teacher plugged into the PUENTE Center's digital classroom via videoconferencing equipment in South Central Los Angeles. The center's aim, which is to prepare residents of Boyle Heights for the workforce, has proven so successful that many communities around the Los Angeles area are seeking to emulate PUENTE's programs in their neighborhoods.

Any resident with the desire to explore can cross the threshold into the digital world provided by PUENTE. In this community, the distance once bridged by foot, word-of-mouth, social connections, automobiles, employment services, and more has been collapsed into a screen and a convenient and accessible place to view it. This is exactly the content and the infrastructure that is required for digital places to be successful. The objective is not to follow a "build and they will come" design philosophy, but to identify specific community needs, create access to the available digital resources, and teach the skills necessary to use them efficiently. In a telling commentary on the continued importance of physical contact, over 70 percent of those participating in a national survey noted that having a "convenient and comfort-

PUENTE LEARNING CENTER

While community technology centers are often bootstrapped together in the best grassroots fashion, they nonetheless provide an important public place for digital access and learning. A model, state-of-the-art facility is the PUENTE Learning Center in Boyle Heights, California. PUENTE, which means "bridge" in Spanish, is an acronym for "People United to Enrich the Neighborhood Through Education." It is, in fact, a bridge to resources and skills available across the digital threshold.

A key figure in the founding and growth of PUENTE has been Sister Jennie Lechtenberg. A lifelong educator with thirty years of experience in parochial schools, she founded PUENTE in 1985 to provide after-school learning opportunities for children as well as their parents.[1] First established in the balcony of an old Masonic Temple, the center has become a community focal point for computer-based access and education, having served some 12,000 residents in this predominantly Hispanic enclave of Los Angeles.

Through the tireless efforts of Sister Lechtenberg and her staff and supporters the center now occupies a 40,000-square-foot building designed by Stephen Wooley, complete with 350 workstations.[2] An estimated 2,000 students (young and old alike) use the center each day. After-school learning is available in the Children's Computer Lab; language courses through the English as a Second Language (ESL) classrooms; and office software training through a mock corporate office environment. The Center has also established distance learning sites in South Central Los Angeles, and provides ESL training through a remote videoconferencing hookup.[3]

The Center's aim, which is to prepare residents of Boyle Heights for the workforce, has proven so successful that it has become a national model for successful community-based technology learning. A visit to the PUENTE Learning Center reveals an energy that

able place to go" was an important draw for those using community technology access centers.[44]

CROSSING THE DIGITAL THRESHOLD

Digital places can also enhance cultural and scientific inquiry through innovative threshold connections. Over the last decade, several new interactive museums, especially science museums, have provided a new digital place threshold for informal and cultural learning. Robert Steeper of San Francisco's Exploratorium notes that "the cardinal feature of these new science centers has been the development of interactive exhibits and educational program-

PHOTO BY AUTHOR

cannot be captured by awards, articles, or pictures; the energy is contagious because it is literally wired into a digital community with more resources than any one locality could provide. As one twenty-two-year-old former resident of Mexico City and now avid PUENTE learner told a *Los Angeles Times* reporter, "When I came to California I couldn't speak a word of English . . . my goal this year is to learn it all. I will speak English."[4] And PUENTE will provide the setting and the technology to make his goal reachable. ◀◀

1 For a short history of PUENTE see http://www.hudson.org/ncpcr/Programs/puente.html.
2 Kelly Wilson, "The PUENTE Learning Center: A Building and a Program," *Journal of Urban Technology* 5, no. 2 (1 August 1998): 47-60. Additional information available at the architect's website: http://www.swassoc.com.
3 PUENTE program information is available on its website: http://www.puente.org.
4 Michael Quintanilla, "Bridge to a Life of Literacy," *Los Angeles Times*, 10 December 1995, E-1.

ming key to the idea that learning is an active enterprise."[45] A recent review of fifty interactive museums by IEEE Spectrum provided support for the notion that interactivity (often digitally based) is a critical part of the learning experience.[46] A related study found strong connections between science centers and local schools and universities, a connection enhanced by programs such as Illinois's Museum in the Classroom project, which brings artworks and lectures into the classroom via web exhibits.[47, 48]

A recent addition to the intersection of technology, culture, and community is the new children's museum, The Zeum, in San Francisco, which was completed in 1999. According to project architect Bruce Prescott of Adele

Naude Santos and Associates, "We wanted technology to be a central feature of the museum. Of course, when we first proposed the design, we weren't sure what the technology would be." Begun with a strong video component, the museum now features a range of interactive exhibitions. Most significant, electronic technology is built into the overall social activities program for the museum. In one major display, children make their own electronic movies, with the lights dimming and the show premiering every half-hour. Transformative designs are coming of age with Generation Y (see Figure 3.10).

The Benton Foundation supports digitally connected arts projects throughout the United States. Its projects build on local efforts to use the Internet to enhance cultural communication.[49] Project sites allow local artists to create and maintain a presence across the digital threshold. A recent assessment of an Internet-artist network in Los Angeles confirmed that it was helpful in promoting a sense of community.[50] Significantly, there was more interest in information about how the network could be used to connect to

Figure 3.10. Production place in The Zeum children's museum.

the local physical community than to the virtual space alone. Similarly, one of the most popular activities determined by the survey was "web raisings," a "hands-on" workshop where community groups and artists come together to learn how to create their own websites. (The opening photograph to this chapter shows a raising in the Los Angeles area.)

CONCLUSION: RECOMBINATIONS FOR COMMUNITY MEANING

During the closing decades of the twentieth century there was an erosion of traditional public space due to a number of technological, sociological, and economic trends. Malls replaced town squares; gated communities replaced traditional neighborhoods; parking lots replaced open spaces. Writing about these trends in *Suburban Nation,* architect and new urbanism advocate Andres Duany and his coauthors summarize the situation we now face: "The choice is ours: either a society of homogenous pieces, isolated from one another in fortified enclaves or a society of diverse and memorable neighborhoods, organized into mutually supportive towns, cities, and regions."[51] Contrary to the notion that technology can only foster isolationism, innovative electronic networks can encourage the development and growth of accessible, civically engaged communities. They can add a new dimension to public space, one that interacts with and supports physical space.

While much has been made of recent commercial interests in digital communities (see John Hagel and Arthur Armstrong's *Net Gain* for creating loyal online customers), the creation of vibrant place-based communities should not be left strictly to the market forces of the private sector.[52] Rather, local communities can play a crucial role in defining the nature and types of electronic-community services available to their citizens. The major thrust of this chapter has been to demonstrate how local public institutions such as schools, libraries, and community centers can play a key role in creating digital places at the community level. While communities of interest will continue to thrive on the Internet, this will not erase the need to carve out free digital space to facilitate the interactions of local communities.

While the exact contours of specific new digital communities depends on local circumstance, the strands of recombinant design suggest several important features: they can represent innovative recombinations of uses (*fluid locations* for learning, culture, and health care); they can retain the traditional role of civic institutions (*meaningful places* such as libraries and schools); they can have synergistic virtual and physical dimensions (*threshold connections* to allow access from anywhere); and they should be crafted in a manner that facilitates local and user access and participation (*democratic designs* of community access).

RECOMBINANT DIGITAL COMMUNITIES

Like homes, workplaces, and commerce, community functions are recombining. In designing and redesigning digital communities, some items to consider include:

■ *Schools.* School officials can explore the community connections that can be enhanced by combining school network development and lifelong learning to support educational and training needs throughout the community. Teachers can exploit new bandwidth connections in the home to encourage enhanced connections with children and parents in the community. Higher education (both community colleges and universities) can investigate new technology-infused partnerships with businesses and students.

■ *Libraries.* Local libraries can consider how new and innovative designs can help them reassert their spatial and electronic presence in the community, including universal access to all community members. New partnerships can be explored with other community resources—museums, schools—to devise innovative electronic and physical "third-places."

■ *Museums and Cultural Centers.* Community and cultural groups can develop new interactive dimensions to their exhibitions and programs to enhance local electronic cultural presence and community. These can include taking an active role in getting local artists represented as well as connecting citizens and visitors to local cultural museums and organizations.

■ *Community Institutions.* Nonprofit community groups can work with local schools, libraries, city officials, and the private sector to evaluate access needs and devise training and learning programs. Local governments can consider those government services that can be provided electronically and play a role in ensuring access to residents. Local officials can also consider mechanisms for using the electronic medium to enhance face-to-face participation in local debates and decisions.

Recent experience suggests that communities will benefit by leveraging the activities of traditional civic enterprises, such as libraries, schools, and museums, through electronic networks. These institutions provide points of entry and access.[53] The school is no longer just a school but a learning center with strong electronic connections to the home. The museum is no longer a self-contained institution, but can provide a network for artists throughout the community. The library is not just a repository, but a dynamic "third place" for communicating and learning. Taken together, new connections can create a web of activities that, in sum, create community.

NOTES

1   William Jefferson Clinton, State of the Union Address, 21 January 2000, Washington, D.C.

2   See http://www.ntia.doc.gov/otiahome/tiiap/index.html for a listing of demonstration projects supported by the Clinton Administration. Also, see http://www.sl.universalservice.org for an overview of projects supported by the federal e-rate program.

3   See Spiro Kostof, "Public Places of Today," in *The City Assembled: The Elements of Urban Form Through History* (Boston: Little, Brown, 1992), 172-188.

4   Sara M. Evans and Harry C. Boyte, *Free Spaces: The Sources of Democratic Change in America* (Chicago: University of Chicago Press, 1992), 17.

5   Peter Rowe, *Civic Realism* (Cambridge: MIT Press, 1997), 9.

6   For the planning of "anchoring institutions," see William Morrish and Catherine Brown, *Planning to Stay* (Minneapolis: Milkweed Editions, 1994).

7   Introduced in Thomas Horan, "A New Civic Architecture," *Journal of Urban Technology*, vol.7, no. 2, August 2000. See also Anita Blanchard and Thomas Horan, "Virtual Communities and Social Capital," *Social Science Computer Review* 16 (1998): 293-307.

8   See, for example, "The Web Maestro: An Interview with Tim Berners-Lee," *Technology Review* 99, no. 5 (July 1996).

9   See Peter Rowe, *Civic Realism* (Cambridge: MIT Press, 1997); Richard Sennett, *The Fall of Public Man* (New York: W.W. Norton, 1974).

10 Kenneth Gergen, *Saturated Self: Dilemmas of Identity in Contemporary Life* (New York: Basic Books, 1991), 215. Additional details provided at presentation given at Claremont McKenna College, Claremont, California, October 1995.

11 Robert Putnam, *Bowling Alone: The Collapse and Revival of American Community* (New York: Simon & Schuster, 2000), 245.

12 Barry Wellman, "The Networked Community," in *Networks in the Global Village: Life in Contemporary Communities* (Boulder, CO: Westview Press, 1999).

13 http://www.perseus.tufts.edu/GreekScience/Students/Ellen/ Museum.html#RTFToC11.

14 Sarah Klein, "Community News Focus: Countywide, Bid to Recoup Library Funding Gets Support," *Los Angeles Times,* 15 March 1996, B3.

15 Conducted for Lake Research and the Tarrance Group by Opinion Research Corporation in Princeton, New Jersey, between 12-18 April 1996.

16 *Buildings, Books, and Bytes: Libraries and Communities in the Digital Age* (Washington, D.C.: Benton Foundation, November 1996), 2.

17 Walter Crawford and Michael Gorman, "Future Libraries: Dreams, Madness, and Reality" (Chicago: American Library Association, 1995).

18 Lorrie LeJeune, "Before Its Time: The Internet Public Library," *The Journal of Electronic Publishing* 3, no. 2 (1997). Available at http://www.press.umich.edu/jep/03-02/IPL.html.

19 Peter de Jonge, "Riding the Wild, Perilous Waters of Amazon.Com," *New York Times Magazine,* 14 March 1999, sec. 6, 38.

20 Peter Lyman, "What is a Digital Library," *Daedalus* 125, no. 4 (Fall 1996): 4.

21 Cynthia Ripley, *San Francisco Public Library Post-Occupancy Evaluation Final Report* (San Francisco: City of San Francisco, 4 January 2000).

22 Jason Chervokas and Tom Watson, "A Quiet Revolution at the Library," *New York Times,* 10 June 1996. See http://www.nytimes.com/pages-technology/cybertimes/index.html.

23 "$125-Million Safdie Project in Vancouver," *Architectural Record* 180, no. 7 (July 1992): 21.

24 See http://www.vpl.vancouver.bc.ca/branches/librarysquare/home.html#tour.

25 Gary Wolf, "The Unmaterial World," *Wired,* June 2000, 308-319.

26 Sarah Parrott, "Future Learning: Distance Education in Community Colleges," *ERIC Digest* ED385311 (May 1995). Available at http://www.ed.gov/databases/ERIC_Digests/ed385311.html.

27 Robert Lenzner and Stephen Johns, "Drucker: Seeing Things as They Really Are," *Forbes,* 24 March 1997, electronic edition. Available at http://www.forbes.com/forbes/97/0310/5905122a.html.

28 See Katherine Culp, Jan Hawkins, and Margaret Honey, "Review Paper on Educational Technology Research and Development" (New York, Center for Children and Technology, January 1999). Also Margaret Honey, Katherine Culp, and Fred Carrigg, "Perspectives on Technology and Education Research: Lessons from the Past and Present" (Prepared for the Secretary's Conference on Educational Leadership, Washington, D.C., 12-13 July 1999).

29 "Union City School District, Union City Online: An Architecture for Networking and Reform: Year Two Progress Report," available at http://www.union-city.k12.nj.us/virtual-tour/frame_7.html.

30 Laura Wernik, project architect, e-mail correspondence, 8 December 1998. See also http://www.hmfh.com/hrut.html.

31 George Gilder, "The Issaquah Miracle," *Forbes ASAP,* 7 June 1993.

32 For the Issaquah technology history, see http://www.issaquah.wednet.edu/district/technology.html.

33 John Gilles, "If the Students Lead, the Teachers Will Follow," *Grade School Upgrade,* available at http://www.zdnet.com/zdtv/thesite/0697w2/work/work596_061097.html.

34 Other prominent examples of educationally oriented community networks include the Blacksburg Electronic Community, the Davis Community Network, and the Vineland Community System in Vineland, New Jersey.

35 J.L. Gogan and P.J. Guinan, "Case Study: Fletcher Allen Health Care's Telemedicine Initiative," Babson College, 1998. Report available at http://www.vtmednet.org/telemedicine/case.html.

36 Michael Ricci, Peter Callas, and William Montgomery, "The Vermont Telemedicine Project: The First Six Months," *Telemedicine Journal* 3 (1997): 94.

37 For a full account of the Well, see "The Epic Saga of the Well: The World's Most Influential Online Community," *Wired,* May 1997.

38 Arthur Armstrong and John Hagel, "The Real Value of Online Communities," *Harvard Business Review,* (May-June 1996):134 ; see also O'Reilly & Associates (eds.), *The Harvard Conference on Internet and Society* (Cambridge: Harvard University Press, 1977), 438-439.

39 See Douglas Schuler, *New Community Networks: Wired for Change* (New York: ACM Press, 1996); Andrew Cohill and Amy Kavanaugh, eds., *Community Networks: Lessons from Blacksburg, Virginia* (Boston: Artech House, 2000).

40 Clifton Chow et al., "Impact of CTCNet Affiliates: Findings from a National Survey of Users of Community Technology Centers," report for the National Science Foundation (Newton, MA: Community Technology Centers' Network, July 1998).

41 Bruno Guissomo, "A Year and a Half Later, a Wired Neighborhood Looks Back," *New York Times,* 13 October 1998.

42 Clifton Chow et al., "Impact of CTCNet Affiliates: Findings from a National Survey of Users of Community Technology Centers," report for the National Science Foundation (Newton, MA: Community Technology Centers' Network, July 1998). Also, National Telecommunications and Information Administration, *Falling through the Net: Defining the Digital Divide* (Washington, D.C.: U.S. Department of Commerce, July 1999).

43 Ibid.

44 Westat, "Evaluation Report: Telecommunications and Information Infrastructure Assistance Program, 1994 and 1995" (Conducted for U.S. Department of Commerce, Washington, D.C., July 1999).

45 Robert Steeper, "Science Museums as Environments for Learning," *Physics Today* 43, no.11 (November 1990): 50-56.

46 Trudy Bell, "U.S. Science and Technology Museums," *IEEE Spectrum* (September 1995). Available at http://www.spectrum.ieee.org/publicaccess/0995muse.html.

47 Inverness Research Associates, *An Invisible Infrastructure: Institutions of Informal Science Education* (Washington, D.C.: Association of Science-Technology Centers, 1996).

48 Lorilee Huffman, Jennifer Earls, L.M. Wood, "Museum in the Classroom: Integrating Museum Artifacts and Technology" (Paper delivered at Museums and the Web: An International Conference, Toronto, Ontario, Canada, 22-25 April 1998).

49 See http://www.openstudio.org.

50 Anita Blanchard and Thomas Horan, "L.A. Culture Net Evaluation Final Report" (Claremont, CA: Claremont Graduate University Research Institute, June 1999).

51 Andres Duany, Elizabeth Plater-Zyberk, and Jeff Speck, *Suburban Nation: The Rise of Sprawl and the Decline of the American Dream* (New York: North Point Press, 2000).

52 John Hagel and Arthur G. Armstrong, *Net Gain: Expanding Markets Through Virtual Communities* (Cambridge: Harvard Business School Press, 1997).

53 *Moving Toward More Effective Public Internet Access* (Washington, D.C.: U.S. Commission on Library and Information Science, November 1998).

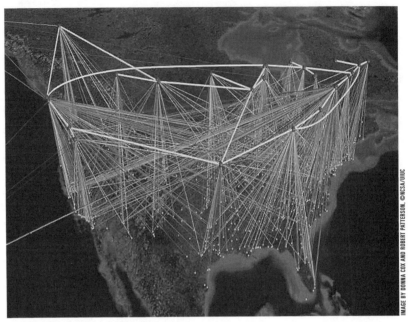

Images of the Digital City: Cybergeography.

IMAGE BY DONNA COX AND ROBERT PATTERSON, ©NCSA/UIUC

CHAPTER 4

WIRING
LIVABLE REGIONS

I N *DIVIDED HIGHWAYS* historian Thomas Lewis vividly portrays the ways in which the ambitions of highway policymakers and engineers nearly ruined several city centers, including the French Quarter in New Orleans, the Fenway area of Boston, and the Wharf area of San Francisco.[1] In each case, a combination of factors, including overenthusiasm for the value of new highway improvements and underappreciation for the links between cultural and economic vitality of urban enclaves, placed these vibrant urban places on the brink of disaster in the late 1960s and early 1970s.

As a consequence of this unfortunate chapter in transportation history, a series of federal planning and democratic participation requirements must now be followed before any such infrastructure can be built.[2] Indeed, a focus on a city's "hard" infrastructure is now seen as a narrow view because it connotes a city as strictly a machine, an engine of input, production, and output. Rather, the city can instead be seen as having social, economic, and cultural attributes that are affected by, yet transcend the supporting infrastructure. This "soft" infrastructure is at least as important as the "hard" infrastructure, as it plays an equally critical role in ensuring a high quality of life throughout large and small communities.[3]

In this vein, it is useful to recall the insights of urban theorists and observers like Kevin Lynch and Jane Jacobs, who wrote of the city as a complex representation of physical, cultural, social, and cognitive associations between a place and its dwellers.[4] For example, they helped us understand that a city street corner is not just an intersection of two roadways, but also a social place (where people on the street meet), an economic place (where local businesses operate), a cultural place (a site of historic significance), and an environmental place (a source of air and noise pollution to be mitigated).[5] The city can be seen as a mosaic of settings and modalities—a "collage city" in the words of urban theorists Colin Rowe and Fred Koetter [6]

Chapter 4 examines the emergence of recombinant design in the context of this metropolitan mosaic. Like the transportation infrastructure, the digital technology infrastructure is having a broad impact on regions throughout North America. A unique aspect of this new infrastructure, however, is the strong role played by the private sector in producing and delivering not only the physical apparatus, but an assortment of digital technology jobs and opportunities. Fueled by the Telecommunications Deregulation Act of 1996 and the explosive use and investment in Internet-related product and services, regions around North America are recombining to take part in the new economy. Drawing upon the principles of recombinant design, this chapter addresses questions such as: what are the implications of fluid and footloose economic networks on regional places? What is the value of a sense of place in this emerging footloose economy? What threshold connections are possible between electronic infrastructures and regional amenities? What is the role of public policy in ensuring that wired regions remain livable and provide digital access to all of their residents?

These questions can be answered by addressing the broad impacts of telecommunications on cities. New York University's Mitchell Moss and Anthony Townsend succinctly summarize our challenge: "Telecommunications technologies are being studied within a framework that fails to recognize the powerful way in which new communications technologies are transforming the basic components of cities and the activities within these urban spaces, as well as the spatial distribution of urban regions."[7] In keeping with this observation, the conceptual lens for considering this transformation focuses on how regional attributes—economic, physical, social, natural—provide a foundation for developing regional recombinations of space and place. Such an approach is consistent with the findings of Harvard's Michael Porter, U.C. Berkeley's AnnaLee Saxenian, and others, who have found that technology-based industries are, in fact, quite dependent on the quality of regional features.[8]

Ultimately, preserving the unique characteristics and natural qualities of these regions requires a compromise between economic ambitions and social, cultural, and environmental values. For example, many of the country's fast-growing second-tier regions—Portland, Austin, Seattle, Minneapolis—are following a range of "smart growth" policies that combine incentives for high-density infrastructure improvements to attract businesses with aggressive open-space and growth-boundary actions to preserve environmental amenities. This context for smart growth provides an important land-use condition for considering the development of a digital region, which should also be livable in terms of its land-use development.[9]

CONNECTING HISTORY, TECHNOLOGY, AND THE FUTURE

Digital technologies do not write on a tabula rasa of regional identity and circumstance, but often represent the latest wave in technological advancement to inject changes in a region. Historically, key geographic elements and existing infrastructure defined the growth of Boston as a seaport city, Chicago as the railroad and skyscraper city, and Los Angeles as the automobile and defense-industry city.[10] Now, digital technology is playing a significant role in re-creating cities, and doing so in a manner that draws upon their unique characteristics. Once again, the importance of place-making comes to the fore as high-technology companies decide where they want to develop their businesses.

While all cities represent some combination of place, technology, and people, it is fitting to look toward the "cradle of technology," Lowell, Massachusetts, for a revealing illustration of how digital technology combines with regional elements to produce economic and cultural value. Lowell represents a rich mix of history, technology, and culture, held together by a strong regional educational system, reasonable cost of living, supporting transportation and telecommunications infrastructure, and active involvement by both the public and private sector in city affairs. These dynamics comport with the notion of recombinant design (see feature box below).

PLACE AND THE NEW ECONOMY

The saga of Lowell over the last century reveals, among other lessons, that *fluid locations* is a strong strand at the regional level, as businesses have in-

---

LOWELL: THE HISTORICAL RECOMBINATIONS

Located near a key resource of the industrial age—the intersection of two rivers—Lowell, Massachusetts, led the country's entry into the Industrial Revolution through a unique combination of local infrastructure (the river and canals), technology (industrialized factories), and regional talent (the largely young female farming labor pool from across New England). At its peak in 1850, there were 50,000 people working in six different Lowell mills.[1]

But by the turn of the century, the tide had turned, as southern regions became more competitive. Lowell's economy then declined over the next fifty years, until the mainframe computer explosion in the mid-1960s. The resurgence of Lowell in the 1960s was aided by the transportation infrastructure—Boston's outer loop—that connected the regional high-tech labor pool, attracting industries such as Wang Laboratories to locate their corporate headquarters in the industrial town.[2] By the 1980s, once again the competitive advantage of other regional economies and companies (this time Silicon Valley) led to the loss of high-tech jobs and the bankruptcy of Wang Laboratories.

Indeed, the Wang headquarters has served as a symbol of the city's fortunes. Built at an estimated $80 million in 1975, the company's towers bustled with activity during the 1970s. After the bankruptcy of Wang, the towers were eventually sold for $525,000, a fire-sale price, in 1984.[3]

Today the buildings, renamed Cross Point, are a highly valued symbol of economic rebound for Lowell and New England. They are occupied by twenty-two new businesses that offer health care, banking, telecommunications, and Internet access, a dynamic mix of entrepreneurial high-tech start-ups and business that have reinvigorated Lowell. To some

---

creasing flexibility to locate almost anywhere. The rise of global telecommunication networks has made businesses extremely footloose. Whereas establishing a new mill required a site that was adjacent to a geographically fixed river (hence, the regional advantage of Lowell), today many businesses can locate across a much wider geographical grid than before, supported by the increasing ubiquity of telecommunications infrastructure. The need for economies of localization (to be near resources) has given way to economies of urbanization (overall amenities of a region, such as the quality of the workforce), and economies of globalization (far-flung networks of production, distribution, and consumption).[11]

---

locals, like Convergent CEO John Thibault, the continuing evolution of Cross Point parallels his own evolution in the industry. He first started there when it was Wang Laboratories, then led software company Gotell to the public markets and arrived at his current position in spring 2000. All companies were based out of Cross Point in Lowell.[4]

In short, after a century of creation and re-creation, Lowell embodies a hard-fought recombination of local attributes, cultural history, and public and private investment participation.[5] As you stroll through downtown Lowell, you get a palpable sense of its industrial past, from the European-based ethnic neighborhoods to the mills that have been reinvigorated as an urban national park. A drive on the freeway reveals the current digital technology cluster that is driving the economy—the parking lot of the refurbished Crosspoint once again full of cars. Other towns around Massachusetts are seeing these full parking lots and realizing their own versions of recombinant design, including Clock Tower Place in Maynard (home of Monster.com) and the Massachusetts Innovation Center in Fitchburg.[6] ◀◀

1 See Laurence Gross, *The Course of Industrial Decline: The Boott Cotton Mills of Lowell,Massachusetts, 1835-1955* (Baltimore: Johns Hopkins University Press, 2000). Also John Reps, *The Making of Urban America* (Princeton, NJ: Princeton University Press, 1992); John Coolidge, *Mill and Mansion: A Study of Architecture and Society in Lowell, Massachusetts, 1820-1865,* 2nd ed. (Amherst: University of Massachusetts Press, 1993).
2 Sara Rimer, "For Chilly New England Economy, Spring," *New York Times,* 17 March 1997, A1.
3 "Geometry Affiliate Sells Interest In Cross Point for Nearly $100M," *Commercial Property News,* 31 August 1998. Available at http://www.cpnrenet.com/breknews/oldnews/aug3198/geometry.html.
4 Brian Cook, "Ex-Cisco Executive Finds He Can Go Home Again," d*business.com,* 5 May 2000. Available at: http://www.dbusiness.com/Story/Print/0,1197,BOS_110045,00.html.
5 See Patricia O'Connor, "Lowell's Resurgence Gives Optimists Hope," *New Bedford Standard Times,* 10 October 1996. Available at http://www.s-t.com/daily/10-96/10-06-96/m01lo051.html.
6 Brian Cook, "Old Mill Being Transformed Into $30M Incubation Center," *dbusiness.com,* 2 May 2000. Available at http://www.dbusiness.com/Story/0,1118,BOS_103583,00.html.

GLOBAL ENCLAVES: VALLEYS TO ALLEYS

Within this globalized economy, a new set of powerful centers has appeared in regions that take advantage of the fluid nature of the electronic marketplace and the resources of major metropolitan areas. Indeed, one could argue, as Saskia Sassen does in *The Global City,* that the power of place becomes more, not less, concentrated as one moves to the scale of global economic transactions.[12] She observes, "Economic globalization and the new information technologies have not only reconfigured centrality and its spatial correlates, they have also created new spaces for centrality. We are seeing the formation of a trans-territorial 'center' constituted via telematics and intense economic transactions. The most powerful of these new geographies of centrality at the interurban level binds the national and international financial and business centers: New York, London, Tokyo, Paris, Frankfurt, Zurich, Amsterdam, Los Angeles, Sydney, and Hong Kong among others."[13] While the emerging telecommunications networks could, in theory, allow global financial transactions to be conducted from anywhere, this has not been the case.

THE CHANGING MIX OF MONEY AND PLACE

As has been chronicled by sociologist Manuel Castells, the "space of flows" (see Chapter 1) provides new cleavages of finance and power; in his words "the global financial markets, and their networks of management, are . . . the mother of all accumulations."[14] With roughly the equivalent of the U.S. gross domestic product traveling through electronic currency channels every week, the rise of these global markets is presenting policy and management challenges, such as ensuring stable markets amid fluctuating, day-to-day political and economic events. However, often lost in the analysis of global cities and world markets is how a region's unique mix of qualities finds its way into the global financial marketplace.

Regional digital economies have not developed uniformly, but through a number of interlocking economic enclaves with corresponding physical representations. Such enclaves include "Silicon Valley" in Palo Alto and San Jose; "Silicon Beach" on Los Angeles's Westside; "Silicon Alley" in New York; and

"Multimedia Gulch" in San Francisco. While undoubtedly a mix of real activity and marketing hype, these "siliconia" nonetheless reveal the evident value of physical proximity and place-based social and economic networks.[15] Through recent analysis of Internet business locations by Matthew Zook and others, this connection has been established, showing a strong metropolitan bent to the Internet economy (see Figure 4.1).[16]

During the industrial era, Wall Street served as both a real place and a metaphor for the power of place; that is, the complex economic valuations of companies brought to a single electronic place, the New York Stock Exchange. Today, with new companies growing in the new economy, Silicon Valley has replaced Wall Street as the financial watering hole. The number of venture capital firms and technology headquarters that are located in the Valley is nothing short of phenomenal; approximately one-third of all venture capital investments in the United States were made by Silicon Valley firms to Silicon Valley businesses.[17] It remains the locus of the technology industry, housing corporate headquarters for Intel, Sun, Oracle, and Apple, top companies

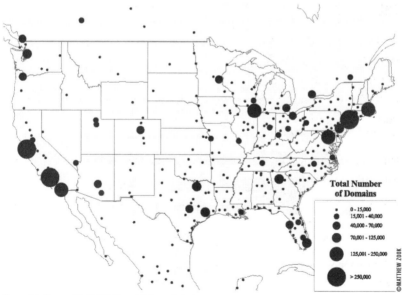

Total Number of Domains

- 0 - 15,000
- 15,001 - 40,000
- 40,000 - 70,000
- 70,001 - 125,000
- 125,001 - 250,000
- > 250,000

©MATTHEW ZOOK

Figure 4.1. Geographic distribution of dot-com industry.

whose combined revenues were at least six times that of top companies in Austin, Boston, or other comparable cities.[18]

The major challenge facing the Valley, of course, is maintaining quality-of-life amenities (schools and housing) in the face of continued competition from other regions. To do so, the public and private sector joined together to create a cooperative planning and resource network, a "nonprofit civic incubator," known as Joint Venture.[19] Notes its president and CEO, Ruben Barrales, "The emergence of 'clusters' of Internet companies in other regions around the country clearly indicates that other factors play a crucial role in attracting and retaining Internet companies. To remain the leader of this vital industry, Silicon Valley needs to shore up its relative advantages and address the internal challenges that can undermine our competitive position." A study commissioned by Joint Venture went on to identify a handful of competitive regions and the key factors that business will consider when selecting a location, which include access to quality labor, presence of related industries, telecommunications infrastructure, and quality of education.[20] Even Silicon Valley has to constantly reinvest in its hard and soft infrastructure to retain its competitive advantage (see Figure 4.2).

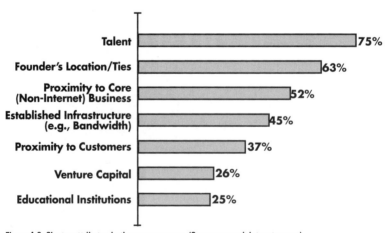

Figure 4.2. Cluster attributes in the new economy. (Source: www.jointventure.org)

MULTIMEDIA ENCLAVES

One of the competitive regions identified by Joint Venture in Silicon Valley is "Silicon Alley," which is centered in and around New York's downtown.[21] Lower Manhattan is undergoing its own recombinant design, taking advantage of the geographic proximity of major media industry, financial institutions, and new media start-ups as well as the cultural attributes of the SoHo and Wall Street areas. As reported by PricewaterhouseCoopers, there are some 6,000 new-media companies operating on the south end of Manhattan.[22] Anchored to the north by traditional media companies like Time-Warner and NBC, Silicon Alley has become a leader in a range of new media and Internet companies including iVillage, n2k, and others.[23] A widely publicized study by Coopers and Lybrand in 1997 first identified 23,000 new media jobs in Lower Manhattan. A recent update by PricewaterhouseCoopers has found that since this time, the new media industry has continued to expand, growing by 136 percent between 1997 and 2000, with the greatest concentration of new media companies now in an area ranging from Lower to Midtown Manhattan.[24] As noted in an earlier discussion of 55 Broad Street (see Chapter 2), many nascent Internet media businesses benefit from close physical proximity in New York City. The recent survey results confirm the value new business placed on both "soft" and "hard" urban infrastructure: access to talented workers and high-quality technological infrastructure were viewed as the two most valued attributes. A number of zoning and tax law changes, beginning in the early 1980s, facilitated the resurgence of innovative live-work arrangements, which in turn helped Manhattan's new media enclave to emerge. The high cost of doing business in Manhattan, however, remains a concern among many new media firms.

A similar phenomenon in the entertainment industry is occurring on the west coast, where the Westside area of Los Angeles is booming as a strong multimedia center, propelled, in part, by the largest U.S. electronic export: movies. The locational value of the Westside is buoyed by the ongoing boom of the entertainment industry, resulting in the presence of both high-bandwidth networks and skilled digital workers near the core media production enclaves.[25]

Within the sprawling Los Angeles region, a Burbank/Hollywood/Westside digital nexus has become a significant force in Los Angeles's continued growth as a multimedia force. Over the last decade, the growth in the entertainment industry fueled Los Angeles's economic resurgence, and this growth occurred despite the decline of the aerospace industry and without the arrival of a major new studio.[26] Instead, the region witnessed the rise of interlocking digital networks, from the growth of postproduction facilities—like Digital Domain—on the Westside to the expansion of studios—Universal, Warner Brothers, NBC, Disney, and CBS—outward toward Burbank and Glendale. Underlying this migration to various enclaves in Los Angeles has been the establishment of a high-bandwidth network capable of electronically linking each phase in the preproduction, production, and postproduction filmmaking processes.[27]

Small postproduction facilities like Swietlik, Inc. have moved to Santa Monica because, as Dan Swietlik succinctly put it, "this is where the industry is now."[28] Large studios like Dreamworks SKG realized it was better to rely on the network of facilities in the Los Angeles region than to build their own. The entertainment industry is now a complex recombination of physically and electronically based processes, most of which retain a strong link to and reliance on the amenities of the Los Angeles area. Those amenities include access to a large, skilled workforce, financing and technological infrastructures (including a high-bandwidth video transport system), and a climate amenable to year-round filming.[29] And it is these very features that are propelling Los Angeles's evolution from entertainment industry hub to converged entertainment/new media/Internet industry hub.[30]

THE RIGHT STUFF: COMMAND AND CONTROL CITIES

While global cities represent highly visible recombinations of space and place, many more subtle recombinations and emerging patterns of growth are occurring across a range of medium-sized metropolitan regions. To use demographer William Frey's phrase, a new set of "command and control" cities, which are physical "production" cities with strong corporate services and complex information management dimensions, have emerged. Between 1960

Figure 4.3. Technology-fueled small city growth in the United States. (Source: Milken Institute)

and 2000, job growth swelled in a host of second-tier regions including Austin, Seattle, Charlotte, Phoenix, Minneapolis, and Denver; the growth of high-wage information technology firms has exerted an unmistakable influence on this economic surge.[31]

These information- and technology-intensive cities have been dubbed "tech-poles" by Milken Institute's Ross DeVol. While major cities (San Jose, New York, Boston, Los Angeles), not surprisingly, are the highest ranking "tech-poles," his analysis also uncovered significant growth in smaller cities in the United States (see Figure 4.3). DeVol notes that "further examination of the fastest growth in high-tech industries reveals a high mix of small- to medium-sized metros that are developing some concentration of these industries. Most of the metros (thirty-eight out of the top fifty in high-tech growth) are in the South and West, and they rank high on most measures of cost of doing business, cost of living, and the elusive concept of quality of life."[32] Supporting the notion of this technology-infused development, DeVol and his colleagues also analyzed the contribution of high-tech industries to the growth of metropolitan regions over a ten-year period; they found that second-tier cities had a higher proportion of their growth attributable to high-technology industries than to any other

LIVING THE GOOD LIFE IN AUSTIN

Michael Dell once proudly stated, "Every time I go to Silicon Valley, I thank God that we are based in Texas."[1] And for good reason. Austin has a lower cost of living than northern California. Wages for software programmers with equal experience are approximately 25 percent lower in Austin than in Silicon Valley. The city has the third largest percentage employment growth in the country, after Las Vegas and Raleigh-Durham-Chapel Hill. Partly because of its early concentration on the computer chip business, Austin entered the software industry later than other locales, but it is quickly developing software and multimedia expertise. The city increasingly depends on its 425 software companies, which together employ 33,000 people. This is in addition to the established semiconductor industry, which employed 26,000 in 1995 and is also expected to grow.[2]

Austin's success in attracting high-tech businesses is due to a variety of factors, including a critical mass of related industries, a low cost of living, a mild sun-belt climate, and a business-technology-friendly government. But, according to local officials, the most important factors were the concentrated efforts by public officials and entities, including the University of Texas at Austin. A vibrant university, which now spends $1.4 billion annually on research, played a critical role in attracting high-tech businesses. Ranked as the number-one regional economy by *Forbes* in 2000, the overall picture that emerges is one of a region that has successfully balanced the "hard and soft attributes of a new economy."[3]

The challenge for Austin is to continue its high-technology growth, but in a manner that is consistent with its own aggressive "smart-growth" policies. While companies such as Dell have tended to grow on the outskirts of the city, policymakers have recently had success in getting firms such as Computer Sciences Corporation and Intel to locate in their downtown "desirable development zone."[4] In this manner, Austin holds promise for not just high-tech growth, but high-tech growth done in a smart-growth manner. ◀◀

1 "Deep in the Heart of Texas," *The Economist*, 29 March 1997, S14.
2 Forecasted for 1997-2002 in DRI/McGraw-Hill, top 20 U.S. Metropolitan Areas for Employment Growth, http://www.dri.mcgraw-hill.com/framecon.html.
3 Tim W. Ferguson and William Heuslein, "Best Places," *Forbes*, 29 May 2000. Available at http://www.forbes.com/forbes/00/0529/6513136a.html.
4 Ann Slayton Shiffler, "Mixed Use Catches On in Downtown Projects," *Austin Business Journal*, 5 June 2000. Available at http://www.bizjournals.com/austin/stories/2000/06/05/focus6.html. For information on Austin Smart Growth, Desired Development Zone Incentives, see: http://www.ci.austin.tx.us/smartgrowth..

market sector.[33] Seattle, Albuquerque, Boise, and Austin (see "Living the Good Life in Austin," page 101) represent a new breed of high-tech, high-amenity cities.

Various rankings have been compiled on the best "wired cities," and while the ordering may change year to year, cities such as Austin, Cambridge, Palo Alto, Minneapolis, or Seattle, which share common characteristics, are always on the list.[34] Each of these cities has aggressively parlayed regional distinctions into a competitive advantage in one or more industry clusters: banking for Charlotte; services and software for Minneapolis; manufacturing and software for Austin.[35] While these distinctions exploit local circumstances and fortune (e.g., that Michael Dell started his business while at the University of Texas at Austin), industry clusters are only part of a successful equation that matches quality local features (skilled workforce, adequate infrastructure, cultural amenities, low cost of living, local demand) with the needs and desires of a fast-growing segment of the digital economy.[36]

In sum, the value of local features plays an integral role in enhancing the regional value of place in a globally oriented digital economy. Consequently, economic development policy should now be focused on enhancing the "hard" and "soft" infrastructure requirements of high technology firms.[37] For example, the state of Colorado has launched ambitious plans, actions, and institutes to advance its telecommunications and information technology industry, including the development of a statewide telecommunications plan and the establishment of a workforce-training institute. In addition, the state has vowed to make government more responsive by implementing numerous e-government services, such as electronic filing of state income taxes and e-business platforms for working with vendors.[38] The paradox, then, is that increased economic mobility increases the importance of establishing new connections between the economic power of global transactions and the enduring value of local places, including the appropriate role of local, regional, and state agencies in enhancing this value.[39]

DIGITAL THRESHOLDS FOR URBAN CULTURE

While digital technology is playing a crucial role in the growth of regional economies, it is also beginning to play a role, at least indirectly, in displaying, communicating, and encouraging the cultural components of city life. At the most basic level, highly skilled technology employees also tend to be better educated, and this can enhance demand for a range of cultural amenities. Moreover, as discussed in Chapter 2, many new start-ups benefit from the live-work orientation of city life and this has contributed to a resurgence in urban living. These trends represent new possibilities for reinventing urban areas as the center of culture, commerce, and social life advocated by the City Beautiful movement of a century ago. A steady trend of urban rejuvenation has ignited downtown enclaves across the United States in the last decade, from SoHo in New York, Lowertown in Minneapolis-St. Paul, SoMa in San Francisco, Detroit Lofts in Detroit, and the Old Bank in Los Angeles.

The redevelopment of Yerba Buena Gardens adjacent to the Moscone Convention Center in downtown San Francisco has attracted a recombinant mix of technology, culture, and commerce. This two-block urban redevelop-

---

RECOMBINANT LIVING SOUTH OF MARKET

Named for its location South of Market Street, the SoMa area of San Francisco has been subject to numerous redevelopment attempts over the past fifty years and is only now reemerging as an economic and cultural force—and digital technology is playing an important role. Some 400 Internet and digital technology companies have offices in SoMa, ranging from large operations like Macromedia and *Wired* magazine to an assortment of small start-ups.[1] SoMa's mixed-use fabric features a variety of innovative living arrangements, including a host of trendy live-work lofts. The connection to digital technologies is clear. Many of the lofts are being used to support small innovative business developments. As one SoMa developer put it, "Start-up companies prefer cool-looking space, shorter-term leases, and spaces that are prepared for occupancy. We like to think that we are as close to plug-and-play [Internet-ready] as possible as all of our buildings have T-1 and T-3 communications available and the individual spaces are wired with cat-5 cabling."[2]

Figure 4.4. Sony Metreon complex.

USED BY PERMISSION: YERBA BUENA ALLIANCE

ment carefully balances art (several museums), commerce (Sony Metreon), urban gardens (the Yerba Buena Gardens), and Technology (the theme of the Metreon and The Zeum children's museum; see "Recombinant Living South of Market," page 102). It can be seen as a variant of the same factors of recombination that influenced Lowell, Massachusetts (albeit with a decidedly Californian flair). Both redevelopments have a strategic digital economy location presence (Cross Point in Lowell; "Media Gulch" in Yerba Buena), both have a meaningful cultural dimension (Boott's Mill; the San Francisco Museum of Modern Art), and both have had extensive public and private investment. Of course, the urban entertainment aspect of Yerba Buena Gardens provides a distinctly late-twentieth-century element to the enterprise, while Lowell remains rooted strongly in its industrial past.

Figure 4.5. Interactive Levi's store.

But SoMa is more than a recombinant live-work enclave; it is reinventing itself as a new digital threshold for urban entertainment. Yerba Buena Gardens, an arts and entertainment complex organized around a public green, embraces technology as part of its experience. As discussed in Chapter 3, this includes The Zeum children's museum. It also includes the mammoth Sony Metreon entertainment retail complex that anchors the southern edge of the gardens. A principal theme throughout the Metreon is the intersection of technology, entertainment, and retail, from the Discovery Viewing Center to the Interactive Levi's store. There is no question that Yerba Buena Gardens has recombined its elements to bring together culture, commerce, and the natural environment. Of course, it may turn out to be too much of a good thing. Concern has now turned to ensuring that high-tech start-ups don't drive out the artists and ethnic communities that made SoMa attractive in the first place.

1 Julie Schmit, "Multimedia Magnet Pulling Top Talent To San Francisco," *USA Today Technology Report*, 28 February 1999.
2 Michael Ross, email correspondence, 17 July 1998.

Figure 4.6. Switches versus people in downtown Los Angeles.

Whether these mixed-use, public-private developments represent a resurgence in urban life or a misleading indicator of more sprawling consequences of technology-fueled growth depends on a number of factors. Within the urban context, one immediate challenge is balancing the renewed demand for innovative live-work arrangements with the parallel mushrooming of demand for switching facilities or collocation ("co-lo") hotels, large facilities that house telecommunications switching and Internet hosting equipment. Similar to the controversy that confronted highway development efforts in the 1960s, the use of downtown real estate is being debated; the key issue is how to balance the positive economic value of these equipment-oriented facilities with parallel interests in developing more people-intensive businesses (including Internet start-ups) and their spillover impacts on local commerce and livability. In Los Angeles, for example, some 150 telecommunications providers have located near the local telephone company switching station (see feature box on page 4). While this has helped to absorb an excess inventory of commercial office space, it is viewed by proponents of a more livable downtown as hurting their efforts to make the city more vibrant; switches don't buy coffee or go to local theater productions (see Figure 4.6). While the "switches versus people" issue has perhaps been most visible in downtown Los Angeles, similar telecommunications deregulation-driven developments appear to be occurring around the country.[40] Local business and community groups need to devise reasonable compromises to ensure that "co-lo" hotels do not drive out the people, and vice versa.

Another land-use issue pertains to larger regional impacts. From an economic point of view, the new telecommunications infrastructure facilitates the movement of telecommunications- and Internet-related jobs to metropolitan areas, though this need not be limited to the urban core. Mitchell Moss has observed that a key characteristic of digital regions is connectedness, and this includes connectivity across electronic and transportation dimensions.[41] While it is convenient to think that e-commerce begins and ends with the click of a cursor, in reality this "business to consumer" transaction sets off a chain of supply-side events, eventually resulting in the delivery of the merchandise. The recent growth of e-commerce warehouses on the outskirts of metropolitan areas and near commercial airports underscores an important land-use development.[42] Working to ensure that the current transformation of the e-business purchase, supply, and distribution chain is done in a manner that supports regional land use and environmental policies is yet another regional policy matter requiring attention. Environmental analyst Nevin Cohen has proposed several steps businesses can take to advance an environmentally responsive e-commerce supply system, ranging from paperless confirmations to alternative fuel use by e-commerce deliverers.[43]

Perhaps the most daunting challenge that lies ahead is affecting the location decisions of high-technology businesses, particularly at the periphery of metropolitan areas. While growing technology corporations often have understandable demands for large parcels of contiguous land, effective land-use policy would help balance business-related development throughout metropolitan regions rather than just at the periphery. Positive examples of responsive high-technology development include the Sun Corporation's location of its New England regional headquarters in a redeveloped brownfield site along I-495 in Burlington, Massachusetts, and Austin's success in persuading Computer Sciences Corporation to locate their regional headquarters in the city's downtown instead of a suburb or greenfield.[44]

In sum, the emergence of digital hubs in metropolitan areas requires a recombinant design approach to balance the economic "hard" infrastructure with the "soft" social, cultural, and environmental attributes of regions. Over the last several years, smart growth policies have increasingly influenced alternative development patterns. While definitions of smart growth vary, common themes include adaptive use of existing urban areas, protection of open space, innovative live-work environments, public-private partnership initiatives, and incentives for mixed-use development.[45] The challenge now is to harness the enormous economic power of the high technology industry in order to meet broad regional goals such as have been articulated in several regional smart growth policies and initiatives.

PLANNING THE DIGITAL CITY: ACCESS FOR ALL

Whether in Lowell, San Francisco, Austin, or elsewhere, the principle of *democratic design* suggests the need to consider access to the fruits of the Internet- and telecommunications-driven economic boom. The Telecommunications Deregulation Act of 1996 set the framework for a strong private sector role in providing the infrastructure for this new information superhighway, but many regions are realizing that the private sector cannot be counted on to provide the infrastructure that is needed to reach all citizens. Rather, there is, in fact, a public interest in ensuring an adequate telecommunications infrastructure, not only for economic growth but for citizen access as well.

It is fitting that the public sector step forward, because, as with previous technological gains—electricity, telephones—there are communities that will trail in the adoption and benefit of the infrastructure unless aggressive policy action is taken. Despite a decade-long economic boom in the 1990s, low-income areas did not realize gains in terms of income and wealth compatible with other areas; in 1997, there were still 35 million people in the United States living below the poverty level.[46] As noted in Chapter 1, a recent report by the U.S. Department of Commerce demonstrates the extent to which computer ownership and access varies. Figure 4.7 provides additional infor-

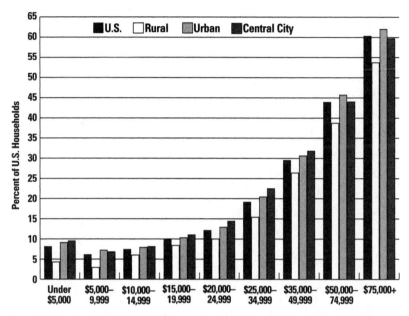

Figure 4.7. Percent of U.S. households with access to Internet, based on income and location. (Source: NTIA, 1999)

mation from this report, highlighting the extent to which Internet access varies by income and, to some extent, location. Of households that make under $35,000 per year, less than 15 percent have active Internet access, and the figure is even lower for those who live in inner-city and rural areas, or are black or Hispanic. While there are many factors contributing to this inequity of access, the specter of a "digital divide" signals the need for public economic development policies that ensure universal access to broadband services. This need has found partial support in the E-Rate provision of the Telecommunications Deregulation Act. Through this provision, and related federal demonstration programs, a number of community programs have been established to encourage high-bandwidth access and community use in low-income areas.

The implications of the Department of Commerce report are myriad. Within the context of recombinant urban design, the report provides an important reminder that plans for designing digital regions need to consider the needs and interests of all residents and citizens—for how else are democratic designs possible?

There are several emerging examples of regional digital place design that feature the goal of ubiquitous access. For example, the State of Minnesota is taking aggressive action to provide high-bandwidth access to rural and urban residents and businesses. Dubbed "Connect Minnesota," the project will provide high-bandwidth connectivity throughout the state—a feat achieved through the artful trading of highway "right-of-way access" to the telecommunications industry, in return for fiber-optic access throughout the state. Variants of the Minnesota plan have or are being considered in other heavily rural regions, including Kentucky, Iowa, and Wisconsin.

In urban areas, the issue is often not lack of bandwidth, but lack of opportunities for residents to economically benefit from the flourishing new industries. While the record on technology industry investment in the inner cities is rather thin, there are several examples of new investment patterns.[47] Tim Draper's Zone Venture, a path-setting example of inner-city investment, is a venture capital fund specifically aimed at incubator businesses in the downtown Los Angeles area.[48] In Chicago, a recent publicly led initiative has sought to extend high-bandwidth connectivity throughout the metropolitan area (see feature box on page 128).

The southeastern portion of the United States remains one of the least-served regions from an infrastructure perspective, suffering from a variety of location-oriented limitations of access to infrastructure and training. Consequently, analyses such as Progressive Policy Institute's State New Economy Index places Louisiana, West Virginia, Arkansas, and Mississippi as the lowest-ranking states in terms of high-technology capacity. Their report, however, puts a positive spin on the situation: "While lower-ranking states face challenges, they can also take advantage of new opportunities. The IT revolution gives companies and individuals more geographical freedom, making it easier for businesses to relocate, or start up and grow, in less densely populated states, farther away from existing agglomerations of industry and commerce. But a key policy challenge will be to find a way to extend advanced telecommunications infrastructure to these places."[49] A coordinated effort is needed containing many attributes: improved hard infrastructure (telecommunications, transportation), improved soft infrastructure (education, cultural amenities), and the aggressive development of public-private partnerships such as Netscape founder Jim Barksdale's $100-million education initiative in Mississippi.[50]

CONCLUSION: WIRED AND LIVABLE

In contrast to the highway expansion programs of the 1950s, the community context for digital deployment strategies tends to place a greater weight on using the technology to emphasize local features, history, aspirations, and visions over more clinical infrastructure engineering calculations.

Just as a *sense of place* is a driving concept for digital settings and a *sense of community* is an important construct for digital communities, a *sense of regional identity* can be an influential construct for digital cities. Once again, the power of place has not evaporated, but revealed its importance in new and changing ways.

Digital design implications flow from the desire to preserve regional qualities while enhancing the overall economic value of the region. In terms of public sector policy, there is a need to craft high-technology economic development policies that not only ensure adequate "hard" infrastructure for e-commerce development, but the "soft" infrastructure that will retain the attractiveness of a region. Often these policies require collaboration across various agencies (transportation, telecommunications, education) and levels (local, regional, state) of government. Examples of useful policies include broadband telecommunications efforts in Minnesota, urban economic development incentives in downtown Los Angeles and lower Manhattan, corporate location incentives in "smart growth" areas such as Austin and Portland, and training initiatives in Colorado.

The private sector also plays an important role, because the location decisions of companies are of critical importance to a region's economic development. High-tech business can take a leadership role in commercial development in a manner that is consistent with overall economic and land-use goals. There are, no doubt, more "smart" decisions that can be made every day. In aggregation, these decisions produce lasting economic, social, and en-

Figure 4.8. *Forbes,* 4 November 1996, 220-221.

vironmental impacts on a region. As environmental psychologist Dan Stokols observes, the information-rich nature of many of our settings creates a parallel need for "restorative environments" to regenerate the senses.[51] The emergence of high-technology places reaffirms the value of natural environments: we need a place to unplug. A recent advertisement in *Forbes* magazine astutely captures the benefits of protecting the natural environment (see Figure 4.8). While we can live anywhere, we will want to live somewhere, and natural beauty is an enduring value of place, even in the digital era.

NOTES

1   Thomas Lewis, *Divided Highways: Building the Interstate Highways, Transforming American Life* (New York: Viking Press, 1997).

2   Thomas Horan, Hank Dittmar, and Daniel Jordan, "Transportation Policies for Sustainable Communities," in *Toward Sustainable Communities: Transitions and Transformations in Environmental Policy,* D. Mazmanian and M. Kraft, eds. (Cambridge: MIT Press, 1999).

3   For a short but cogent discussion of soft and hard infrastructures in the new economy, see Mike Hollinghead, *Small Rural Communities in the New Economy* (Edmonton, Alberta, Canada: Facing the Future, 1995). http://www.worldbank.org/devforum/study_hollinshead.html.

4   Kevin Lynch, *The Image of the City* (Cambridge: MIT Press, 1960); Jane Jacobs, *The Death and Life of Great American Cities* (New York: Random House, 1961).

5   As Spiro Kostof noted, "More than a mere traffic channel, the street is a complex civic institution, culture-specific and capable of dazzling formation variation and calculated nuance." *The City Assembled* (Boston: Bulfinch Press, 1992), 220.

6   Colin Rowe and Fred Koetter, *Collage City* (Cambridge: MIT Press, 1984).

7   Mitchell Moss and Anthony Townsend, *How Telecommunications Is Transforming Urban Spaces* (New York: Taubman Urban Research Center, March 1998).

8   Michael Porter stresses, among other elements, the importance of regional networks, amenities, and clusters; for example, see Michael Porter, "Clusters and the New Economics of Competition," *Harvard Business Review* 76, no. 6 (1997): 77-90. AnnaLee Saxenian stresses regional economic networks and culture as an important contributing force; see AnnaLee Saxenian, *Regional Advantage: Cultural Competition in Silicon Valley and Route 128* (Cambridge: Harvard University Press, 1996).

9   While individual elements of the smart growth agenda can be debated on their merits for a particular region, the general trend is toward crafting a range of infrastructure, land-use, and economic development policies that balance economic, social, and environmental priorities. For a summary of smart growth and related debates see http://www.smartgrowth.org.

10 See Peter Hall, *Cities in Civilization* (New York: Random House, 1999).

11 Robert Atkinson, "Technological Change and Cities," *Cityscape: A Journal of Policy Development and Research* 3 (1998): 129-170.

12 Saskia Sassen, *The Global City: New York, London, Tokyo* (Princeton, NJ: Princeton University Press, 1993).

13 Saskia Sassen, "Electronic Space and Power," *Journal of Urban Technology* (1998).

14 Manuel Castells, *End of Millennium* (Oxford: Blackwell Publishers, 1996), 343.

15 For a listing of various siliconia see http://www.tbtf.com/siliconia.html.

16 Mathew Zook, "Internet Metrics: Using Hosts and Domain Counts to Map the Internet Globally," *Telecommunications Policy* (forthcoming, 2000); also see Martin Dodge's Atlas of Cyberspace at http://www.geog.ucl.ac.uk/casa/martin/atlas/atlas.html.

17 For example, in the second quarter of 1999, $2.6 billion was invested in Silicon Valley-based companies, representing 34.8 percent of total venture capital investment for that quarter. See PricewaterhouseCoopers, "Moneytree Survey," http://204.198.129.80, 1999.

18 John Micklethwait, "Survey Silicon Valley: The Valley of Money's Delight," *The Economist,* 29 March 1997, 5. Also "Top 100 Information Technology Companies," *Business Week,* 2 November 1999.

19 See http://www.jointventure.org.

20 Joint Venture, *Internet Cluster Analysis* (San Jose: Joint Venture, July 1999).

21 The report identified seven competitive regions: Seattle's Silicon Forest, San Francisco's Multimedia Gulch, Los Angeles's Digital Coast, Austin's Silicon Hills, Boston's Route 128, New York City's Silicon Alley, and Washington, D.C.'s Silicon Dominion.

22 *The New York New Media Industry Survey* (New York: PriceWaterhouseCoopers, 1997).

23 John Pavlik, "Content and Economics in the Multimedia Industry: The Case of New York's Silicon Alley," (New York: Center for New Media, 1997). Available at http://www.columbia.edu/~jp35/lectures/lect_3_1.html.

24 *Third New York Industry Survey: Opportunities and Challenges to New York's Emerging Cyber-Industry* (New York: PricewaterhouseCoopers, March 2000). Available at http://www.nynma.org/files/survey2000.pdf.

25 For an analysis of the locational development of industries in Los Angeles, see Allen J. Scott, *Technopolis: High-Technology Industry & Regional Development in Southern California* (Los Angeles: University of California, 1993).

26 Joel Kotkin, "Southern California in the Information Age" (Claremont, CA: La Jolla Institute Report, June 1997).

27 Elizabeth Douglass, "Telecom Breaks in to Show Biz," *Los Angeles Times,* 12 July 1999, C-1.

28 The Swietlik example and related quotations are from Tenaya Hart, "Digital Technology and Urban Design: A Case Study of Swietlik" (UCLA-Westwood class report, Spring 1998).

29 The high-bandwidth network options are summarized in Gail Lawyer, "There's Gold in Them Thar Hollywood Hills, Competitors Come West to L.A. in Droves," http://www.x-changemag.com/.

30 Joel Kotkin, "Southern California in the Information Age" (Claremont, CA: La Jolla Institute Report, June 1997).

31 William H. Frey, "Metropolitan America: Beyond the Transition," *Population Bulletin* (Washington, D.C.: Population Reference Bureau, 1990).

32 Ross DeVol, "U.S. High-Technology Changes" (Santa Monica, CA: The Milken Institute, 1999).

33 Ibid., 70-78.

34 See for example, "The Hottest Tech Cities," *Newsweek,* 9 November 1999.

35 See also Mitchell Moss, "Telecommunications and the Cities," *Cityscape: A Journal of Policy Development and Research* 3, no. 3 (1998).

36 See Glenn Ellison and Edward Glaeser, "The Geographic Concentration of Industry: Does National Advantage Explain Agglomeration," *Papers and Proceedings of the 111th Meeting of the American Economic Association* 89, no. 2: 311-16 (1999).

37 Dennis A. Rondinelli, James H. Johnson, Jr., and John D. Kasarda, "The Changing Forces of Urban Economic Development: Globalization and City Competitiveness in the 21st Century," *Cityscape* 3, no. 3 (1998).

38 For a summary of Colorado initiatives, see http://www.state.co.us/govoit/index.html.

39 Michael Porter, "Cluster and Industries," *Harvard Business Review* (1997).

40 See Catherine Reagor, "Teleco Hotels," *Urban Land* 59, no. 5, May 2000, 38-43.

41 Mitchell Moss, "Why Cities Will Thrive in the Information Age," in *ULI on the Future: Cities of the 21st Century* (Washington, D.C.: ULI–the Urban Land Institute, 2000).

42 See James Carberry, "Chain of Supply," *Urban Land* 59, no. 5, May 2000, 70-73, 100-103.

43 Nevin Cohen, *Greening the Internet: Ten Ways E-Commerce Could Affect the Environment* (New York: Inform Research, 2000).

44 William Roche, "Corporate Appeal," *Urban Land* 59, no. 5, May 2000, 40-51; "Intel Asked to Grow Smart," *Austin Business Journal,* 17 January 2000.

45 For an overview of smart growth, see David O'Neill, *Smart Growth: Myth and Fact* (Washington, D.C.: ULI–the Urban Land Institute, 1999).

46 U.S. Bureau of Census, 1998.

47 Michael Porter, "The Competitive Advantage of the Inner City," *Harvard Business Review* (May-June 1995).

48 See Karen Kaplan, "Downtown L.A. as High-Tech Hotbed?" *Los Angeles Times,* 16 October 1998, C-1.

49 *The State New Economy Index: Summary Results* (Washington, D.C.: Progressive Policy Institute, 1999). Available at http://neweconomyindex.org/states/summary.html.

50 For a complete listing of state new economy policy recommendations see Robert Atkinson, "How Can States Meet the Challenge of the New Economy?" (Presentation to the National Governors' Association Winter Meeting, 21 February 1999). Available at http://www.dlcppi.org/texts/tech/speech_nga.htmrban.

51 See Daniel Stokols, "Human Development in the Age of the Internet," in *Assessment of the Environment Across the Lifespan,* Sarah Friedman and Theodore Wachs, eds. (Washington, D.C.: American Psychological Association, 1999). Also, personal conversation, April 28, 1998.

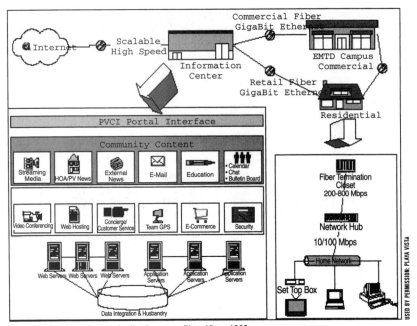

Toward Digital Place Design: Applications map, Playa Vista, 1998.

USED BY PERMISSION: PLAYA VISTA

CHAPTER 5

BUILDING OUR CITY OF BITS

CITYSCAPE DESIGN HAS generated interest and debate since the early Greek city-states, for it both reflects and conditions where and how we live. While the evolution of urban form has been the consequence of many influences, technological advances have played an important role in this changing landscape.[1] The physical arrangement of places and how we communicate across them has evolved from a basic pedestrian scale to a complex assortment of scales and communication patterns.[2] In the United States, it is obvious that technology, seen through the lens of history, contributed to the repainting of the landscape long before the first personal computer arrived on the scene.[3]

The contemporary influences of digital technology are pervasive, having played a significant role in propelling economies throughout North America over the last decade. Increasing exponentially, the bandwidth available through wireline fiber and wireless infrastructures promises still more new possibilities for creating digital places that are both smart and habitable.[4] As I have sought to illustrate in previous chapters, from the design of houses to the development of regions it is hard to escape the economic, social, and environmental footprint of this profound technological change. The strands of recombinant urban design attempt to coalesce several elements of this change in terms of the design of houses, workplaces, communities, and regions we will want to live in. The consequence, one would hope, is the creation of digital places that are intelligent both in the technology that fuels them and the way in which the technology responds to social and community needs.

In this final chapter, I turn from analysis to action. At this point, you might rightfully ask, "What recommendations can be gleaned from previous chapters for designing new settings, communities, and regions?" Good question. While insights from the illustrative examples have been offered throughout the book, it is useful to revisit the strands of recombinant design with an eye toward how they represent themes for designing digital places. Revisiting the strands also provides a stepping stone for considering how we—in our various roles as citizens, consumers, designers, voters, or decisionmakers—can devise our own vibrant digital places.

The chapter is divided into two sections. The first looks at recombinant design themes, which are also summarized in Appendix A. The second section offers seven potential actions for enacting recombinant design themes, as well as a process for determining the most appropriate steps to keep in mind when dealing with particular situations in a community or setting.

RECOMBINANT THEME: DESIGNING FOR MULTIPLICITY

Digital technologies are changing the spatial locations of where we work, play, and engage in public activities. The strand of *fluid locations* highlights the importance of understanding how these arrangements change and complicate the notion of distinct places for distinct activities. This fluidity is expected to increase, with the advent of new wireless services promising an era of near-digital ubiquity. One consequence of widespread electronic access is the need to design for multiplicity—for a more complex assortment of activities across the spectrum of building and community types.

For residential design, this means greater attention should be given to both the integration of digitally based activities throughout the home and the design alternatives for achieving new distributions of electronically mediated work and leisure. As the recent MoMA exhibit, the "Un-Private House," demonstrated (see Chapter 2), this can involve a redefinition of public and private space; work, for example, can remain in a private area or become a pronounced public space within the home. Also, flexible "great rooms" can provide a location for home-based computer work and other, more private functions (family television viewing). Specific wiring guidelines are readily available to facilitate the installation of high-bandwidth residential infra-structure in new developments and wireless networks are increasingly avail-able to existing homes and developments, all of which can accommodate flex-ible use of residential space.[5]

For the workplace, the notion of designing for multiplicity suggests re-thinking the functions of the office in light of new electronic possibilities and related knowledge-work demands for individual and collaborative tasks. New work arrangements need to facilitate different functions—concentrated work, small group discussions, and informal collaborations. These arrangements can include seamless digital connections to the home office environment, be-cause work or some form of computer/Internet use is spilling into the home. High-bandwidth corporate Internets and intranets facilitate a fluid connec-tion between the home and work environments.

At the regional scale, the dynamic of *fluid locations* reveals itself in the paradoxical relationship between digital technology businesses and the re-gions they locate in: while the technology has increased the spatial mobility of business, firms nonetheless have become reliant on the amenities of their regions. In terms of regional design, smart growth is an important land use concept, but has yet to be fully embraced by the explosive and "footloose" high technology and Internet-economy businesses. In the context of recom-binant design, smart growth initiatives should include innovative policies that encourage high-tech business development, and do so in a manner that en-hances the valuable elements of a region—the schools, parks, neighborhoods, and environment (see Chapter 4).

RECOMBINANT THEME: DESIGNING WITH TRADITIONAL PLACE

Most places are meaningful for reasons that have little to do with digital technology. They evoke a subjective *sense of place* or *community*. They convey a circumstance, memory, or purpose. Sometimes these are highly personalized, like a location that served as a setting for a personal life event. Sometimes these are widely shared, such as a major landmark—a bridge, a square, or a promenade. Temple University's Magali Sarfatti Larson observes the delicate balancing act that confronts the designer: "Architecture is a public and useful art. An art that cannot disguise its social and collective origins, for it must convince a client, mobilize the complex enterprise of building, inspire the public, and work with the cultural . . . and symbolic vocabulary not of the client only but of its time."[6]

As articulated by the *meaningful places* strand, digital places represent a functional and "symbolic vocabulary" for linking current needs for technology with broader design objectives for fostering a sense of place and community. The illustrations portrayed throughout the book provide insight into how this laudable goal can be achieved. Digital technologies can be introduced into the home in a manner that respects our "comfort" desires for decompressing, pursuing personal hobbies, or enjoying family time. Digital technologies can be introduced into the workplace in a manner that facilitates but does not replace the value of spaces for face-to-face encounters and collaborative activities. Digital technologies can be introduced into the community in a manner that reaffirms the important role of such institutions as libraries and schools in creating public spaces.

It is important to stress that, in terms of design, the concept of digital places does not erase the need for meaningful building types that pervades everyday life. Rather, the objective is to consider new combinations of electronic and physical place that can accent the various meanings of physical place while introducing a new layer of electronic presence. Homes become places of comfort and electronic engines of production; libraries become storers of print knowledge and community entry points to the electronic world; downtowns become vibrant mixed-use environments and electronically mediated entertainment zones. In terms of public policy, incentives should be enacted that support the adaptive use of historic buildings and districts so that the historical character of local communities can be preserved, while new economy development activities are pursued.

RECOMBINANT THEME: DESIGNING FOR COMMUNITY

A recurring theme of digital place design is the possibility of using technology to build connections within local communities. Public spaces—both real and virtual—provide perceptual and functional meeting grounds for friends and strangers alike. The *meaningful places* strand of recombinant design emphasizes the importance of these spaces, whether real or virtual. These unifying connections, both real and virtual, can help transform a sense of place into a sense of community. Early community networks such as the one in Blacksburg, Virginia, have convincingly demonstrated how community technology infrastructures can aid in making these connections. And a number of community uses are being tested, from connecting neighborhood streets (as Microsoft did in London) to connecting cultural groups (as LA Culture Net did in Los Angeles).

Using digital technologies to reinvent public institutions, such as local libraries and town halls, can create centralized hubs of community activity in our increasingly fractionalized approach to urban design and planning (see Chapter 3).[7] The challenge for our institutions is to use the digital technology to forge new alliances among schools, libraries, museums, and other civic entities in a manner that enhances local interaction. The opportunity exists to create new physical and electronic agoras that will diminish the potentially isolating impact of computer-based work. This can take several forms. Traditional civic institutions (libraries, schools, community centers) can facilitate local information exchange, communication, and Internet access. The New Main Library in San Francisco and the PUENTE Learning Center in Boyle Heights, California, are two of many examples of such access centers. Masterplanned communities provide an interesting opportunity to arrange community access centers in a way that can provide electronic as well as physical "third places" for live-work residents.

There is an important and continuing social purpose to these physical public spaces. Similar to the geographically selective diffusion pattern of electricity and telephone service, not all communities are aggressively being wired by the private sector; telecommunications deregulation continues to disproportionately benefit the high-income sector. The provision of access to all income groups will need to be a public policy concern for the foreseeable future. Left strictly to market forces, inner-urban and rural areas will be slow to receive high bandwidth, will not be a magnet for new-economy jobs, and will risk lagging behind in related economic developments. The recent enactment of several federal, state, and local policies to encourage or subsidize the integration of digital technologies into schools and libraries is recognition by policymakers that some form of government intervention is required to fulfill a social compact on technological advancements.[8]

RECOMBINANT THEME: DESIGNING ACROSS ARCHITECTURES

We increasingly live our day-to-day lives by moving back and forth across the digital threshold between electronic and physical space. For the retail industry, business-to-consumer electronic commerce is providing the most visible interweaving of physical and electronic space. As noted in Chapter 2, points-of-sale have moved from physical stores to electronic locations, and marketing functions have moved from traditional electronic means to include physically based experiences. Retail purchasing has become an interspaced activity that includes electronic and physical browsing, and electronic and physical buying—what real estate analyst Dale Anne Reiss and others refer to as "clicks and mortar" operations.[9] Educational activities are moving to the interspace as well, with distance learning and electronic discussions integrated into place-based activities.

While the electronic and physically based layers of experience are moving together, there is no one design solution for this interweaving. There are many permutations possible to achieve the recombinant design axiom of threshold connections. Some, like product designer and writer Donald Norman, prefer simplified intelligent appliances—that is, making the technology "invisible" and as a part of each component of the built environment, whether it is the television, the refrigerator, or the clock.[10] These stripped-down, single-function devices tend to understate the technology aesthetic, focusing instead on the function to be accomplished. Others, like architects Gisue and Mojgan Hariri propose a transformative fusion between the physical and electronic aesthetic in their imagined Digital House; rather than a traditional design filled with smart devices, the entire house is designed as a billboard for the information age.

These competing views—one stressing the invisible nature of the technology and the other suggesting a distinctive information-age aesthetic—are but two approaches to designing a digital aesthetic. One thing is certain: there is no one stylistic approach that fits all situations. For every traditional library remodeling that quietly incorporates digital features, there is a late-modernist office complex that visibly celebrates digital uses. For some traditional home additions that include an expanded office and home theater, there will be others that choose a new, completely wired digital house. The concept of digital threshold connections does not advance a particular design aesthetic but highlights the need to think through the electronic-physical interface to achieve a desired function and look.

RECOMBINANT THEME: DESIGNING IN COLLABORATION

The experiences of place are not bound by academic or professional discipline; day-to-day activities are a manifestation of our individual and group interests, tastes, and policies. Yet, a common characteristic of modern-day urban planning and public policy is specialization, with coordination across disciplines coming at considerable expense. Such is often the case for digital and telecommunications planning. Observers like University of Newcastle's Stephen Graham and Simon Marvin have found that the design of electronic networks often emanates from a perspective that is narrowly focused on technology, with little regard to related economic, community, and infrastructure issues.[11]

As was introduced in Chapter 1, the "design" approach outlined in the *democratic designs* strand seeks to overcome these artificial barriers by focusing on the desired solution in an integrated manner. First advanced by Donald

Schon and colleagues in books such as *The Reflective Practitioner,* the policy design approach is aimed at bringing together an interdisciplinary group of thinkers and practitioners—"reflective practitioners"—to create inventive solutions to complex situations.[12] Within the context of digital places, the policy design approach suggests the need to involve a range of orientations and constituencies in crafting innovative combinations of physical and electronic space, be it a residential design, a community center, a mixed-use redevelopment, or a greenfield masterplanned community.

The *democratic designs* strand underscores the role of a range of leaders, policymakers, and citizens in designing and building digital places. For many of the projects highlighted in the previous chapters, the starting point is someone articulating a vision that weaves together digital possibilities and physical realities. A century ago, architect Daniel Burnham advocated the use of physical infrastructure planning to rejuvenate city life: "Make no little plans, they have no magic to stir men's blood."[13] Today, electronic and physical planners can test Burnham's dictum through bold visions for arranging space and place. The point of departure is arriving at a vision; the point of execution is translating bold visions into desired applications and design solutions. This process, in a variety of applications, has been followed in a host of communities around the United States.[14]

Digital place planning can be done within the context of a master plan or a facilities or telecommunications plan. It is important to address early in the process the scale of the vision, as this will, among other items, determine the range of participants to be involved in the visioning process. The vision can be small scale, like a computer center in a campus facility, or large scale, such as the design of regional technology infrastructure. The corresponding design elements can include, for example, creating a high-tech-friendly, mixed-use development (including high-bandwidth connectivity); designing a college campus to feature ubiquitous Internet access and communal, face-to-face gathering areas; or developing a new housing mix that features streetside home offices to encourage informal gathering during the day.

Once the scale has been determined, the creation of digital places necessitates the involvement and buy-in of a range of constituents. In the case of the New Main Library in San Francisco, for example, the involvement of various groups became the key to widespread support and fundraising. In the case of Norfolk, Virginia, the development of the municipal telecommunications plan involved focus groups drawn from various public entities: fire departments, city hall, and local schools, among others.[15] In the case of Lock Haven, Pennsylvania, it meant working through the local school system to develop a local network and then reaching out to a range of public and private partnerships to engage the community.[16]

SEVEN ACTIONS TOWARD BUILDING OUR CITY OF BITS

Regardless of scale, it is at the applications level that the attributes of physical places are salient. Digital place design should involve the identification of key sectors that will be affected (residential, commercial, civic, cultural), and then work with those sectors to identify desired services and applications. While I have introduced possible directions for such designs in previous chapters, at this point it is appropriate to provide a sampling of specific actions various stakeholders can take (see also Appendix B). Here are seven actions that can be taken to build our city of bits.

ACTION 1: PROMOTE WIRED LIVE-WORK OPTIONS

Homeowners, developers, and architects should consider how telecommuting or telework can be integrated into the design of residential housing and urban live-work projects. This would include the nature, size, and location of space for conducting home-based computer work and the distribution of high-bandwidth access in the home. As one illustration, the placement of home offices in a manner that has greater street orientation (such as the live-work lofts in Orenco Station) can facilitate digital technology use and an informal public presence. Local policymakers need to attend to issues or concerns about ubiquity of residential access across geographic locations and low-income areas, including implications for providing a community network. Telecommunication providers need to assess how much bandwidth is desired or needed to support innovative residential uses, and they must develop business models to finance it.

ACTION 2: CREATE COLLABORATIVE AND SEAMLESS WORK ENVIRONMENTS

Knowledge work companies need to reestablish the value of physical place by designing workplaces that stress face-to-face activities, such as small group and informal collaboration. Heads-down, private workspaces can complement these club-oriented designs. Information architecture, such as corporate intranets, can enhance the collaborative dimensions and do so across corporate and residential locations. Innovative examples of collaborative environments and seamless electronic environments—such as the Nortel Networks headquarters building—represent the cutting edge of thoughtful designs for work in both the office and the home. Steps can also be taken to better link high-technology work designs to the community fabric. Adaptive use of historic areas, such as is being done in Chicago and downtown Los Angeles, can help integrate the thriving new economy into existing communities.

ACTION 3: LINK BRICKS TO CLICKS THROUGH LOCAL E-COMMERCE

Local businesses need to determine the level of their e-commerce presence. The relationship of the "bricks" and "clicks" sales and supply channels need to be clarified in their business plans to articulate the role of each in advancing the business mission and sales goals. Local businesses and Chambers of Commerce need to consider innovative partnerships to combine electronic and local commerce. Developments such as e-Tropolis Evanston provide innovative examples of ways in which local businesses can exploit the World Wide Web to gain local market share. This would be helpful for many reasons, including the need to understand and plan for the fiscal implications of retail e-commerce on local resources.

ACTION 4: CREATE CONNECTED LEARNING COMMUNITIES

School officials should consider the community connections that can be enhanced by combining school network development and lifelong learning to support regional competitiveness and other civic uses. As demonstrated in communities such as Issaquah, Washington, the electronic architecture of the educational sector can represent an important cornerstone in the provision of high-bandwidth network services throughout the community. Teachers can exploit these new bandwidth connections to the home to enhance their connection with children and parents in the community. Institutions of higher education can explore new technology-infused partnerships with businesses and students to reassert their role in providing service to the community in terms of extended training and learning.

ACTION 5: ENSURE COMMUNITY ACCESS THROUGH LOCAL INSTITUTIONS

Local libraries should consider how new and innovative digital designs can help them to reassert their spatial presence and activate an electronic presence in the community; providing universal access to all local residents is one way to achieve this. As summarized in the Public Library Association's new guidelines for designing wired libraries, the library has evolved from a repository of basic print information to a disseminator of a complex assortment of print and electronic information, the latter requiring a digital planning process of its own.[17] To devise innovative new electronic and physical "third places," this process would need to include a range of partnerships with other community resources such as museums, schools, and community centers. These community resources can become important "third places" for enhancing access to digital technology services and resources.

Community and cultural groups can develop new interactive aspects of their programs to establish or enhance related local electronic networks. Many museums have already taken the first step toward developing a digital connection to their exhibitions and collections. Less common is expanding these networks to feature the work of local artists and topics of interest to arts enthusiasts. This can include taking an active role in getting local artists represented on the Internet as well as connecting citizens and visitors to local cultural museums and organizations.

ACTION 6: PUSH GOVERNMENT TO OFFER E-SERVICES AND E-FORUMS

Local governments should determine which of their services can be provided electronically and explore how to ensure access to their residents. The city can also consider mechanisms for using the electronic medium to enhance face-to-face participation in local debates and decisions. Due to the widespread growth of the Internet, civic forums such as those first advanced by Santa Monica's PEN (Public Electronic Network) and other community networks can now be implemented in cities and towns across North America.[18] Unfortunately, a recent review of thirty-five cities in the United States by the Maxwell School at Syracuse University revealed that most cities have spent the last few years struggling with Y2K instead of conducting more strategic planning and applications development.[19] The timing is now right to extend a range of e-services to citizens, including community news, interactive forums, city council registration processes, ballot information, and, in some instances, voting. The state of Colorado, for example, has organized to pursue aggressively several of these e-government services.[20]

ACTION 7: MAKE HIGH-TECH GROWTH SMART GROWTH

Local economic development authorities and business interests should consider those high-tech segments that would complement the economic goals of the community. New partnerships can be explored with both telecommunication providers and regional planning organizations to coordinate economic growth with regional land-use plans. Possible improvements to the "soft" infrastructure (schools, housing stock, cultural amenities) as well as "hard" infrastructure (telecommunications, transportation) can be considered to enhance regional competitiveness for high-tech jobs. Smart growth policy can provide positive incentives for high-technology industries to locate in places that not only make economic sense but environmental sense.

There are, unfortunately, few examples of major high-tech companies embracing such efficient land use. While urban areas such as SoMa in San Francisco do provide attractive places for many start-up companies, major high-tech corporations seem to prefer campus park settings, albeit within major metropolitan areas. The land-value economics of this preference tends to produce fringe developments such as the Microsoft campus in Redmond, Washington, the Oracle campus in Redwood City, California, Qualcomm Way in San Diego, and the new Cisco campus planned for Richmond, Texas. While such developments provide pedestrian-friendly environments (that is, once you are there), they appear less likely to embrace mixed-use and alternative-transportation-friendly designs. Fortunately, corporations such as Computer Sciences Corporation in Austin are starting to adopt a more sensitive land-use policy. A major and exciting challenge exists to bring high-tech corporations into the fold of the smart growth policy movement.

My seven actions are offered as sampling of how the overall digital place vision and themes can be translated into actions. To proceed with any of these applications, the vision must be squared with the reality of resources and opportunity. Recalling Langdon Winner's admonition in Chapter 1, the vision and application provide the demands upon the system, which citizens, businesses, schools, and institutions bring to the technologists and information architects who will design our digital places consistent with our various and collective desires. The windy city of Chicago provides an interesting example of how these digital designs are being planned and implemented across a host of political settings and circumstances, from a metropolitan planning agency-led study to the Mayor-backed downtown investment fund to a suburban community network (see "Metropolitan Chicago: From Regional Planning to Local Action," page 128).

INFORMATION ARCHITECTURE

While the technology and data capacities will continue to evolve, a digital place plan that contains a vision, desired applications (e.g., the seven steps), and basic electronic architectural foundations can provide the conceptual and technical blueprint for public and private investment in an adequate technological infrastructure.

The development of information architecture for a digital place plan is a complicated endeavor, in part because of the ever-changing and improving range of technological capabilities and services. As nicely summarized by information architect Andrew Cohill, the infrastructure commonly includes elements such as the backbone fiber-based system that connects to the local telephone company or other high-speed connection point (e.g., national service provider), and some form of local high-speed transmission (e.g., wireline or wireless ethernet) to the end user's system (e.g., computer, intelligent

---

METROPOLITAN CHICAGO: FROM REGIONAL PLANNING TO LOCAL ACTION

Ambitious technology plans are underway in the Chicago metropolitan area. Using a metropolitan technology plan as a blueprint, the region has undertaken a diverse array of actions to enhance both the "hard" and "soft" infrastructures needed to succeed in the highly competitive new economy.[1] With strong backing by Mayor Richard Daley, these initiatives include: establishment of a civic network to advance high-speed Internet access to businesses and residents; smart building development with incentives for adaptive reuse of downtown building as technology centers (e.g., the R.R. Donnelly Co. Lakeside Press building); a city-based public-private technology investment fund dubbed "Skyscrapers Ventures."[2]

One outgrowth of these initiatives is the creation of "e-Tropolis Evanston." E-Tropolis aims to provide a complete range of electronic services to the residents and businesses of Evanston, a community of 75,000 (and home to Northwestern University) located approximately thirteen miles from downtown Chicago. These services include high-speed Internet and "smart-building" services, an "electronic city" website to encourage e-commerce transactions with the 3,000 local businesses, and a community center for computer training and service.[3]   ◂◂

1 Patricia Widmayer and Gary Greenberg, "Putting our Minds Together: The Digital Network Infrastructure and Metropolitan Chicago" (Report for the Metropolitan Planning Council, Chicago, September 1998). Available at http://www.nwu.edu/it/metrochicago.
2 A description of the Chicago Technology Initiative available at http://www.ci.chi.il.us/Planning/CITE/index.html.
3 See http://www.evanston.lib.il.us/community/technopolis/index.html.

---

device, personal digital assistant).[21] Bandwidth capabilities continue to evolve rapidly, and the recent onset of high-bandwidth wireless systems and devices suggests we are on the verge of a nearly ubiquitous digital infrastructure. Nonetheless, for each digital place plan, a specific infrastructure plan needs to be developed; this plan translates the desired digital place applications into a network architecture that can support the desired activities.[22] Such a plan is being pursued as part of the Metropolitan Chicago initiative; the city's Technology Development Plan builds on a previous study sponsored by the regional planning agency, and includes a set of actions to ensure high-bandwidth connectivity, as well as the development of parallel civic applications and networks (see Figure 5.1).[23]

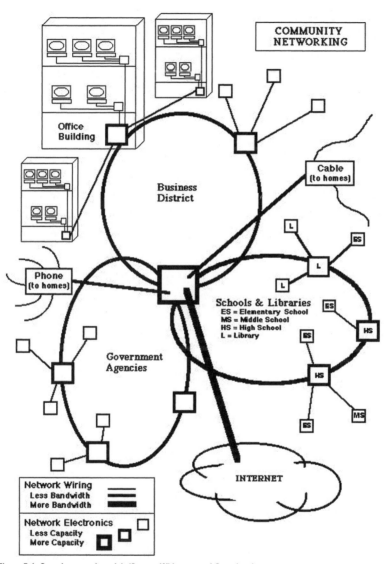

Figure 5.1: Generic network model. (Source: Widmayer and Greenberg)

The ability to create a broadband community network will invariably depend on a host of factors, but should ultimately create a new partnership between the public and private spheres within a community. Public institutions, such as government centers and schools, often serve as useful "points of presence" for community Internet systems, just as they have served as physical cornerstones. Opportunities also exist to create community-specific access centers—unique configurations of learning, culture, and access tailored to local citizen needs.

Communities often need to select among several competing technical alternatives being advanced by competing telecommunications, cable, and Internet service provider (ISP) interests. The development of a digital place plan can provide the applications requirements needed to determine the appropriateness of various technological options.[24] The private sector—telecommunications companies, information service providers, municipal utility companies—have been able to develop a range of technological solutions, skills, and business models to fit a variety of local interests. The Playa Vista project in Los Angeles provides a model for the types of applications that can be considered by new masterplanned communities; it also suggests a process for arriving at digital place partners who can provide the networks and services to the community in collaboration with developers and homeowners associations (see "Getting Wired at Playa Vista," page 131).

NEED FOR POLICY LEADERSHIP

Finally, while many of the key actions to creating digital places reside in the hands of consumers, citizens, and businesses, there is much that can be done in the public sector to facilitate recombinations.

The overriding public policy need is for leadership in creating a cohesive framework for public and private investment in digital technology systems for communities. Within this framework, various sectorial actions—in education, infrastructure, and governance—provide opportunities for recombinant urban design. There are many examples of local community actions, each set off by a range of issues, from economic development (e.g., the Chicago Metropolitan Plan) to telecommunications regulation and access (the Los Angeles Commission) and transportation (the Connect Minnesota project).[25] While the circumstances may vary, the need is the same: timely, accessible, and useful digital services and facilities.

GETTING WIRED AT PLAYA VISTA

Playa Vista is a 1,087-acre masterplanned development located approximately three miles north of Los Angeles International Airport on property formerly owned by Howard Hughes.[1] Occupying one of the largest remaining parcels of land on the city's Westside, the mixed-use development has sought to integrate many state-of-the-art design elements into its plans, ranging from unprecedented (yet controversial) wetlands restoration to bringing giga-bit connectivity to residents and businesses. To determine the best telecommunications system for the project, the developer engaged in a two-tier process: one process solicited the input of a variety of possible telecommunications providers and resulted in the selection of a firm that could deliver converged telecommunications, cable, and data services.[2] The second process involved a broad canvassing of Internet-related business and services about a range of community amenities.[3] As Tom Paradise of the project's developer, Goldman Sachs, observed, "We first wanted to ensure we had the highest bandwidth possible; we are now going about the business of finding quality content and service providers to fill that pipe." The resulting services will include a high-speed community network, Playalink, and a range of e-commerce and community services. ◀◀

1 See Playavista.com.
2 Interview with Robert Picci, Ion Consulting, 2 July 1999.
3 See "Request for Proposals: Telecommunications and Community Intranet Services" (Ion Consulting, prepared for Playa Capital, Chicago, 1998).

While it is true that the Telecommunications Act of 1996 set the general tone of deregulation, there is still a need for policy leadership at the federal level to ensure equal access, including the role of civic institutions in providing this access. While bandwidth availability will eventually make its way into most communities, the need for stewardship in ensuring fairness of access remains high. For at least the short term, the markets have expressed a very strong interest in focusing the design of digital places on those communities that can afford it. For a democratic society such as ours, there needs to be ubiquitous access to remind us, once again, who we are and what we can become.

CONCLUSION: RETURNING TO SONY AND THE SUN

Digital technology systems are now being planned with several design objectives in mind, including reliability, scalability, and affordability, to name a few. The concept of recombinant design of digital places brings forth a new objective: livability. While implicit in many strategic telecommunications planning efforts, the concept of recombinant urban design brings this quality-of-life issue to the fore. And it does so with special attention to the relationship between the electronic and the physical interface.

While the flurry of electronic space development makes it tempting to dismiss the physical arena, there is every reason to believe that functional, enjoyable, and meaningful places will continue to be valued. Indeed, ongoing research on the psychological impact of the Internet suggests that it plays an important role in nurturing social interaction and overcoming the isolating consequences of the technology. Robert Kraut and colleagues conclude their influential *American Psychologist* article on the subject with the following advice: "More intense development and deployment of services that support pre-existing communities and strong relationships should be encouraged. Government efforts to wire the nation's schools, for example, should consider on-line homework sessions for students rather than just on-line reference works. The volunteers in churches, synagogues, and community groups building informational websites might discover that tools to support communication among their memberships are more valuable."[26] In a similar vein, Robert Putnam concludes *Bowling Alone* with the following recommendation: "The key, in my view, in to find ways in which Internet technology can reinforce rather than supplant place-based, face-to-face, enduring social networks."[27]

The choice is ours. The need for physical place and human activity is not going to vanish, but will evolve within the context of digital activities and technologies. Physical place settings can now play an important role in integrating technology-infused activities with the range of other place-based interactions. Multimedia learning environments can encourage electronic and face-to-face communications. Public library-based community access stations facilitate access to printed and electronic information for all residents. Innovative "telework" arrangements facilitate working online at home and spending more time with family and friends. In sum, the proper physical design can become an integral part of deliberately crafting a set of circumstances that facilitate social and community connections. There is no doubt that digital technologies will have an impact on our social and community relations, but how well they integrate with these relations will depend on how well we build our city of bits.

In *The Machine in the Garden,* author Leo Marx examines a writing exercise completed by Nathaniel Hawthorne in the summer of 1844. Sitting in the woods near Concord, Massachusetts, in an area known as Sleepy Hollow, Hawthorne noted the minutiae of his natural surroundings and the sounds of a nearby village—a clock, a cowbell. The scene is suddenly transformed by the piercing whistle of a train, the aural presence of a relatively new technology. Later in the book, Marx remarks on how landscape painter George Inness, in *The Lackawanna Valley,* finished just ten years after Hawthorne's Sleepy Hollow notes, portrays a more harmonious relationship between the locomotive and the countryside—between the pastoral and the industrial landscape.[28] Marx notes: "It [Inness's *Lackawanna Valley*] is a striking representation of the idea that machine technology is a proper part of the landscape."[29]

A new machine, the computer, is in the "garden" of our homes, workplaces, and communities. And, like George Inness's *Lackawanna Valley* landscape, recombinant design aims to find a balance between these places. Just as sunbathers in San Francisco's Yerba Buena Gardens peacefully co-exist next to Sony's high-tech retail behemoth, Metreon (see Figure 4.4), so, too, do digital places aim to balance technology-infused uses with those activities and experiences that remain outside the bits sphere.

The design of digital places is about integrating these new electronic opportunities with the enduring values of physical place. The best and most vivid aspects of life will continue to be real, palpable, and sensory: the thrill of arriving at a beautiful vista, the pungent smells and sounds of urban street markets, the laughter of close friends, the wedding of a loved one, and even a lonely walk through an abandoned drive-in movie theater.

NOTES

1   See Lewis Mumford, *The History of the City* (Orlando: Harcourt Brace, 1961) for an extensive account of the city's history.

2   See Spiro Kostof, *The City Assembled: Elements of Urban Form Through History* (Boston: Little, Brown and Company, 1992).

3   See Peter Hall, *Cities and Civilization* (New York: Pantheon Books, 1999).

4   William J. Mitchell, *E-topia* (Cambridge: MIT Press, 1999).

5   Residential wiring guidelines are available from a number of commercial portals, such as http://www.electronichouse.com/, http://www.electronichouse.com/, http://home-automation.org.

6   Magali Sarfatti Larson, *Behind the Postmodern Façade: Architectural Change in Late Twentieth-Century America* (Berkeley: University of California Press, 1993), 16.

7   See also Douglas Schuler, *New Community Networks: Wired for Change* (New York: Addison Wesley, 1996); Stephen Graham and Simon Marvin, "Planning Cyber-Cities: Integrating Telecommunications into Urban Planning," *Town Planning Review* 70, no. 1 (1999): 89-114.

8   Current information about public and foundation efforts to bridge the "digital divide" can be found at http://www.digitaldividenetwork.org.

9   See Dale Anne Reiss, "From Bricks and Mortar to 'Clicks and Bricks': Companies Face Challenge of Adapting Real Estate to E-Commerce," at http://www.ey.com/global/gcr.nsf/International/Clicks_and_Bricks_-_Real_Estate.

10 Donald Norman, *The Invisible Computer: Why Good Products Can Fail, the Personal Computer Is So Complex, and Information Appliances Are the Solution* (Cambridge: MIT Press, 1998).

11 Stephen Graham and Simon Marvin, *Telecommunications and the City* (London: Routledge, 1996).

12 Donald Schon, *The Reflective Practitioner* (New York: Basic Books, 1983); Donald Schon, *Educating the Reflective Practitioner* (New York: Jossey-Bass 1987); Donald Schon and Martin Rein, *Frame Reflection: Toward the Resolution of Intractable Policy Controversies* (New York: Basic Books, 1994); Richard Boland, "The Epistemology of Design" (Unpublished manuscript, University of Minnesota, 1999).

13 See Thomas Hines, *Burnham of Chicago: Architect and Planner* (Chicago: University of Chicago Press, 1979). Cited in Edward Relph, *The Modern Urban Landscape* (Baltimore: Johns Hopkins University Press, 1987).

14 See Thomas Horan, "Benchmark of Master Planned Communities" (Prepared for Town Development, Claremont, California, 1998). See also http://www.connectedcommunities.net.

15 City of Norfolk, *Information Strategy Plan: Fiscal Year 1999 and Beyond,* Norfolk, Virginia, 22 December 1997.

16 See Bill McGarigle, "Digital Villages Dot the Electronic Frontier," *Government Technology* (February 2000). Available at http://www.govtech.net/publications/gt/2000/feb/coverstory/coverstory.shtm; see also http://www.kcnet.org.

17 Public Library Association, *Wired for the Future: Developing Your Library Technology Plan*, Chicago, Illinois, 1999.

18 Anne Beamish, "Communities On-Line: Community-Based Computer Networks" (MIT Masters Thesis, Cambridge, Massachusetts, 1995). Available at: http://sap.mit.edu/anneb/ cn-thesis/html/toc.html. Also Sharon Doctor and William Dutton, "The First Amendment Online: Santa Monica's Public Electronic Network," in *Cyberdemocracy: Technology, Cities, and Civic Networks*, Roza Tsagarousianou, Damian Tambini, and Cathy Bryan, eds. (London: Routledge, 1998).

19 Maxwell School, Syracuse University, *Government Performance Project: Information Technology*, at http://www.maxwell.syr.edu/gpp/index.htm.

20 For a summary of Colorado's e-government initiatives, see http://www.state.co.us/ gov_dir/gss/imc/colorado_e-govt_vision_vl.pdf.

21 See Andrew Cohill, "The Architecture of Community Networks," in *Community Networks: Lessons from Blacksburg, Virginia*, 2nd ed., Andrew Cohill and Andrea Kavenaugh, eds. (Boston: Art-Tech, 2000), 33-57.

22 Jane Green, *The Irwin Handbook of Telecommunications Management*, 2nd ed. (Chicago: Irwin Professional Publishing, 1996).

23 Patricia Widmayer, "Transforming a Global City for the Information Society: Metropolitan Chicago at the Crossroads," *Journal of Urban Technology* (forthcoming, 2000).

24 For an informative review of various community network architectures, see "Chapter 10: Community Network Technology," in *Community Networks: Lessons From Blacksburg, Virginia*, 2nd ed., Andrew Cohill and Andrea Kavanaugh, eds. (Boston: Art-Tech, 2000).

25 For example, the 1997 NYMA Study recommends seven policies for encouraging live-work arrangements in SoHo.

26 Robert Kraut et al., "Internet Paradox: A Social Technology That Reduces Social Involvement and Psychological Well-Being?" *American Psychologist* 53, no. 9 (1998).

27 Robert Putnam, *Bowling Alone: The Collapse and Revival of American Community* (New York: Simon & Schuster, 2000).

28 For a digital image of George Inness's *Lackawanna Valley*, see the National Gallery of Art OnLine Collections, http://www.nga.gov/cgi-bin/pimage?30792+0+0.

29 Leo Marx, *The Machine in the Garden* (Cambridge: MIT Press, 1967), 220.

APPENDIX A

RECOMBINANT DESIGN: SUMMARY OF PRINCIPLES

RECOMBINANT PRINCIPLES	DIGITAL PLACE IMPLICATIONS Setting Level
FLUID LOCATIONS Theme: Designing for Multiplicity	Residential Design: Create flexible space arrangement for public-oriented digital work functions (including high-bandwidth connections) as well as more private digital entertainment space. Office Design: Address multiple knowledge work needs, providing a range of settings for heads-down, small group, and informal exchanges.
MEANINGFUL PLACES Theme: Designing for Meaning	Office and Residential Design: Recognize the traditional value of office and home for face-to-face exchanges, providing informal meeting areas (offices), and "unplugged" private space at home. Encourage the adaptive use and high-bandwidth wiring of historic buildings for start-up and live-work use. Civic Design: Embrace traditional spaces in civic institutions—such as reading rooms, school courtyards—for complementary "unplugged" vis-à-vis "transformative" functions.
Theme: Designing for Community	Office Design: Create informal working places, perhaps using wireless networks for spontaneous and flexible digital use. Residential Design: Foster innovative placement of home-offices with greater street presence. Civic Design: Encourage development of informal workplaces in and around "third places."
THRESHOLD CONNECTIONS: Theme: Designing Across Architectures	Office and Home Design: Implement high-bandwidth connection to support seamless work across locations, including between home and work as well as e-commerce-retail. Civic Design: Create transformative setting designs that provide seamless interfaces between bricks and mortar and electronic civic functions
DEMOCRATIC DESIGNS: Theme: Designing with Collaboration Access	Civic Design: Create community network access centers in places such as libraries, schools, city halls, and community centers.

ACROSS SETTING, COMMUNITY, AND REGIONAL SCALES

Community Level	Regional Level
Civic Design: Use technology networks to reconnect public spaces—schools, libraries—in a manner that provides networks for communities of place that overcome spatial limitations, as in rural areas.	Regional Policy Design: Encourage high-tech location of business in areas that are consistent with regional growth priorities and land-use concerns about sprawl. Regional Policy Design: Provide incentives for innovative mixed use that can encourage live-work, start-up and local street life.
Civic Design: Reassert the local community value of traditional elements of civic institutions by using them as a locus for community networks. Office and Residential: Design homes (e.g., home offices) to enhance daytime street presence and high-tech offices to be integrated into the (mixed-use) community fabric.	Regional Policy Design: Foster partnerships for the redevelopment of historical areas for high-technology adaptive use. Regional Policy Design: Enhance both hard and soft infrastructure policies that enhance unique community amenities to make regions attractive to high-technology firms.
Civic and Residential Design: Create public-private partnerships to support community networks that serve to connect communities of interest with communities of place. Create new and innovative virtual and real public spaces for community interactions.	Regional Policy Design: Include public institutional elements in a regional telecommunications plan in a manner that enhances distinctive community elements and connections, for example, through the creation of a regional arts network for electronically linking and encouraging local cultural groups.
Civic Design: Use community networks to enhance seamless connection between communities of interest and communities of place. Organize electronic network to aid in accessing community and cultural amenities of local community.	Regional Policy Design: Create comprehensive telecommunications infrastructure that can support high-technology networks. Foster comprehensive electronic presence for governmental and related services.
Civic Design: Use local community networks to discuss pending land-use, ballot, and local election issues.	Regional Policy Design: Encourage public-private partnerships to develop broadband infrastructure that allows for economic development across diverse regions, including inner-city and rural areas.

APPENDIX B

SAMPLE ROLES IN BUILDING OUR CITY OF BITS

Setting Level

INDIVIDUAL ROLES

Worker	Work to obtain company-sponsored high-bandwidth connectivity to workplace from home.
Citizen	Demand that city services be available in civic locations.
Parent	Provide guidance in online versus face-to-face experiences by children.

PRIVATE SECTOR ROLES

Employer	Consider innovative work design options (e.g., "club designs") including capabilities for enhanced telework.
Developer/Architect	Provide new range of residential, office, and public environments. Create "wired" informal settings for collaboration.
Telecom/ISP	Develop high-bandwidth services and networks to enhance ubiquity of access from residential, office, and public environments.

PUBLIC SECTOR ROLES

Schools	Create online capabilities to enhance learning from home. Design public parts of schools to foster community use and lifelong learning.
Libraries/Museums	Serve as renewed location for public access and cultural learning.
Infrastructure Providers	Consider policies for infrastructure that ensure ubiquity of access for all income groups regardless of geographical location.
Local Government	Use planning and land use approvals to encourage innovative residential, office, and retail designs that include adaptive use of historic buildings.

Community Level	Regional Level
Work with employer to encourage innovative public places to allow for informal "third place" work.	Support and participate in workplace activities in mixed-use areas that support high-bandwidth, high-pedestrian environments.
Encourage the establishment of community network for communicating and debating local civic issues.	Insist that economic and land-use planning agencies work together to ensure high-technology economic growth in conjunction with regional land-use goals.
Support and use electronic connections between schools and home.	Support local and regional educational investments in technology.
Create partnerships with local civic institutions in location selection and network design to enhance relationship to community amenities.	Become active in public-private partnerships to enhance regional attractiveness.
Work with communities to reduce isolation through innovative civic designs and community networks that foster public space.	Participate in regional forums for enhancing telecommunications investment and deployment in a manner consistent with land use and economic goals.
Develop innovative community networks.	Become a partner in regional infrastructure development.
Take active role in community networks, such as "point of presence."	Develop educational resource as important amenity to attract new economy businesses and workers.
Take active role in community networks, with special focus on functioning as a location for universal access and getting local culture online.	Link to other cultural institutions (e.g., museums) to enhance access to regional cultural amenities.
Use infrastructure investments to leverage community services and create new community landmarks for the digital era.	Use transport and other infrastructure improvements as means to leverage enhanced capabilities.
Develop local governance structure to provide leadership in telecommunications planning and services. Create easy access e-services for a range of municipal functions and local policy issues.	Create public-private partnerships with telecommunication and digital technology companies to enhance regional competitiveness.